Health
and Social
Education

MAY V. LEA

HEINEMANN EDUCATIONAL BOOKS
LONDON

Heinemann Educational Books

LONDON EDINBURGH MELBOURNE AUCKLAND
TORONTO HONG KONG SINGAPORE KUALA LUMPUR
NEW DELHI IBADAN NAIROBI LUSAKA
JOHANNESBURG KINGSTON

ISBN 0 435 60601 8

First published 1975
Reprinted 1976

To Alec

who has helped me to
become a liberated person

Published by Heinemann Educational Books Ltd
48 Charles Street, London W1X 8AH

Text set in 11pt Photon Times, printed by photolithography
and bound in Great Britain at The Pitman Press, Bath

Preface

This book is intended to be a compendium of ideas for teachers and others interested in health education. It does not pretend to be an exhaustive source of facts. Health education is an emotive subject which needs to be handled carefully and thoughtfully; this book hopes to provoke thought. As health education is a subject of direct personal concern to everyone it can be interesting and exciting and this book tries to stimulate and provide ideas that will make this possible. Where relevant facts are not given in detail there are references, at the end of each chapter, which will enable these facts to be found easily.

Acknowledgements

Whilst the opinions expressed in this book are entirely my responsibility I would like to thank Dr John Rawles and Dr Derek Gill for the help, encouragement, and advice which they have given me so freely throughout the preparation of this book. It is no reflection on them if the advice has not always been taken. I would also like to thank present and past colleagues for their support and co-operation. My thanks are also due to the following for permission to reproduce sections of copyright material:

Hodder and Stoughton Ltd; Corporation of the City of Aberdeen; Pan Books; Ballantine Books; Longman Group Ltd; W. H. Allen and Co. Ltd; Dodd, Mead and Co.; Scott, Foresman and Co.; Health Dept., County of Fife; *The Scotsman*; Royal College of Physicians; *The Lancet*; McGraw-Hill; Hart-Davis MacGibbon Ltd; Jonathan Cape.

Contents

1
Man's Worst Enemy

'Man's worst enemy is himself. He breeds too rapidly. He eats too much. He pollutes his world. He squanders his resources.' So started an advertisement in one of our Sunday newspapers. Is it true? In this book we shall look at the way man treats himself and his environment. We are concerned with health. What is health? The World Health Organization defines it as 'a state of complete physical, mental and social wellbeing'. (Please note the word complete.) By that definition can any of us claim to be healthy? Can we even go so far as to claim that we are healthier than our forbears?

The patterns of disease afflicting mankind have changed remarkably over the last century. Our ancestors suffered from many ills which they did not understand and over which they had no control: they were ravaged by things like tuberculosis, smallpox, diphtheria, and cholera. As they learnt how these diseases were caused so they learnt how to avoid them. Since these diseases are no longer the scourge they used to be, perhaps we should look at the ways in which they were defeated. As this is a health education book I should like to be able to say that the largest factor was the education of the individual. Unfortunately this would not be true; other things played a more important part.

Perhaps the most important role in the improvement of health has been played by the pipe. Not the sort of pipe used for smoking tobacco, but the type used to supply each household with pure water and to remove effluent. Public plumbing has, by the provision of clean water and the collection and treatment of sewage and other refuse, caused a revolution in our standards of hygiene. By making pure water easier to obtain than impure water and by making the safest form of effluent disposal also the easiest, it has ensured a conformity with desirable standards of hygiene that education alone would have had difficulty in achieving.

The other great advance was in the discovery of the way the body protects itself against disease by the production of antibodies—this led to the introduction of vaccination and immunization. But whilst medical science perfected the protection techniques, it was education that persuaded people to accept the protection made available. A great deal of successful health education was carried out by doctors, health visitors, and nurses in making people see the need for, and value of, the protection offered. This individual teaching was reinforced by mass appeals in the form of posters, leaflets, and newspaper advertisements. It was also helped by the ease with which people could get protection. Immunization and vaccination could be obtained free of charge at easily accessible places, such as doctors' surgeries and welfare clinics. Alongside these two advances there was a great deal of other health education. Much of this was individual teaching, carried out in the home by health visitors and district nurses and in surgeries and clinics by doctors. Again the mass media, largely in the form of posters, leaflets, newspaper articles, and advertisements, helped considerably. Little of this would have been possible, however, without the rising standard of literacy amongst the general population, so that although health education did not appear in their curricula, the schools were busy laying the academic foundation without which its success would have been much more difficult. As a result of this individual health education, seconded by some group education especially in clinics, the general standard of hygiene was raised. Spitting in the streets came to be recognized first as a dangerous and then as an anti-social habit. The use of handkerchiefs became general, hand washing more frequent, and the general standards of cleanliness greatly improved. In fact cleanliness was elevated to a place second only to godliness. It has now become a hallmark of respectability to such an extent that young people in revolt against the values of our present civilization are rebelling against our insistence on the need for such rigorous cleanliness. Because of this it is easy for us to forget what a hard battle had to be fought to get people to realize its importance. Today's general acceptance of the need for high standards of cleanliness is a tribute to the success of our health education campaign. But let us not forget the assistance rendered by public plumbing. Piped water and sanitation and the availability of soap and hot water all helped the campaign to succeed. How many of us would be as clean as we are today if we had to wash in cold water with rough unperfumed soap and a complete lack of privacy? We are cleaner than our forbears because we are more privileged as well as more enlightened.

We are clean, we have defeated most of the diseases that killed our forbears and we have removed from our environment many of the more obvious dangers to health. Are we then within sight of the goal of health as defined by the World Health Organization? Any of our more intelligent forbears would have said that, with these improvements both in our environment and in our personal habits coupled with the virtual elimination, in advanced countries, of malnutrition, we should by this time be very near to that goal. Alas we are not! If we were there would be no need for this book. The sad fact is that we are no healthier than our ancestors.

If this statement shocks you, look at the people around you. They live longer, they make dramatic recoveries from serious illnesses, but are they healthier? How many people do you know who are free from headaches, neck or back aches, digestive troubles, sleeplessness, lethargy and depression? How many of your acquaintances manage without the aid of drugs of one kind or another? By drugs I mean alcohol, tobacco, and aspirin as well as L.S.D. and heroin.

No, we have defeated their diseases but managed to raise a whole new crop of our own to replace them. We have controlled the obvious pollutants such as sewage and household refuse and replaced them with modern pollutants such as chemical wastes and exhaust fumes. We have increased life expectancy and so both lowered the general standard of fitness and increased the world population to danger point. In the past it was very much a case of the survival of the fittest; those who were weak or diseased usually died early. Modern medicine now keeps them alive without necessarily being able to make them really fit, and no one is sure what the ultimate result of this will be. By lowering the death rate without lowering the birth rate we have increased the number of people in the world. This is taxing our resources and our ability to deal with increased pollution and is reducing the quality of our lives. If I had to single out one task as of paramount importance in health education, it would be the prevention of the birth of unwanted babies. By preventing unwanted babies, inside as well as outside marriage, we may just be able to avoid legal restrictions on childbearing, but we shall have to work fast or it will be too late.

Let us take a look at some of our new diseases. The greatest killer is heart disease, followed by mental illness, cancer, and accidents. There is one big difference between these causes of death and those that killed our forbears. We have some knowledge of the causes of these killers and many of them are, at least in part, self-induced. It seems almost incredible that intelligent, educated human beings will live in such a way that they are damaging their health and shortening their lives, but most of us do live in this incredible way. Why?

Is it that we don't care whether we are healthy or not, or do we just not believe in our own ability to control ourselves and so our health? We all want to be happy. In fact we all pursue happiness with great vigour. Yet in 1837 the Reverend Sydney Smith said 'I am convinced digestion is the great secret of life'. If we share this conviction, and I do, then we must be either crazy or masochistic to treat our digestive systems as we do. I think that, health fanatics apart, most people regard the pursuit of health as a rather spoil-sport activity. We are emerging from the 'Thou Shalt Not' era of our puritan ancestors into an age in which fulfilment is important to us all. We must be careful not to carry this too far.

If some one drank water which he knew to be infected with typhoid, not because he would otherwise die of thirst, but from choice because he liked the taste, we would consider him insane. How many of us drink alcohol or inhale tobacco smoke and still manage to be accepted as sane members of society?

Further Reading

Brockington, Frazer. *The Health of the Community.* (London: Churchill, 1965.)
Clegg, A. G. and Clegg, P. E. *Man Against Disease.* (London: Heinemann, 1973.)

Hughes, D. T. D. and Marshall, P. T. *Human Health, Biology and Hygiene.* (*Cambridge: Cambridge University Press, 1970.*)
McKeown, Thomas. *Medicine in Modern Society.* (London: Allen and Unwin, 1971.)

2
Who is Responsible for Our Health?

We have a health service that is the envy of much of the world. Our doctors and nurses are highly skilled people. A lot of time and money is spent in order to give them these valuable skills and the equipment they need to use and develop them. Having got this expensive service, these wonderful people, this marvellous equipment, what use do we make of it?

We certainly use our health service; we use it so assiduously that it is in danger of breaking down. There are waiting lists for hospital admission of such alarming proportions that urgent cases are subjected to delays which may even be fatal. Doctors' surgeries are overcrowded and dental treatment is unobtainable in some areas. In addition our chemists' shops are flourishing as they pander to our mania for self-medication. The number of pills and potions swallowed in the United Kingdom in a year is alarming. And yet the number of days lost through sickness every year is increasing and far exceeds the time lost through strikes. What are we to do about it?

We could, of course, increase the money to be spent on the health services. We could build more hospitals, train more doctors and nurses, buy more equipment and produce more drugs. Our hospitals are grossly overcrowded and their staffs are overworked; there is a crying need for something to be done about it. But would even doubling the number of beds really put things right? I have a feeling that Parkinson's law would operate and the number of patients would expand to fill the beds available. If this continued we should, eventually, all be either sick or engaged in looking after the sick. To avoid this ludicrous state of affairs we shall have to take a fresh look at our health services and ask ourselves what we want them to do and what is the best way in which we can spend our money in order to bring about this desired end.

The health service is divided into two main camps, curative and preventive. There are places where they overlap but often they are quite separate. So far our main emphasis has been on curing rather than on preventing. This is very understandable; people who are ill are in obvious and often urgent need of help. There is also the fact that the treatment of the sick, the relief of suffering, and the saving of life provide satisfaction and often drama to those who look after them. On the other hand, the rewards of those working in preventive, medicine are often long-term and undramatic. So it is easier to recruit and to keep staff in the curative branches of medicine than in the preventive ones. What is true of staff is also true of money. We live in a materialistic society where money plays a dominant role. There is never enough of it, except in wartime. What there is is fought for by the different government departments. Governments obtain money by taxation, and they need to be popular if they are to continue to govern – that means that taxes must be kept as low as possible. The amount available for health, welfare, and education is also kept low by the fact that we live in a society so obsessed by the production of material things that it regards these services as 'unproductive'. This, in itself, guarantees a shortage of money, but how do we spend what we have?

In 1972 out of a total of £2267 million spent on the health services approximately £1748 million was spent on the curative services and less than £519 million on the preventive services. The reasons for this are similar to those which cause manpower to be more readily available for the curative branches. It is more dramatic; it is more satisfying; and it is *seen* to be necessary. In the preventive field the rewards are long-term and undramatic and, perhaps most important, there is often no concrete proof of success. If you prevent someone from getting ill it is difficult, in fact impossible, to demonstrate that he would have been ill if the preventive measures had not been taken. Such proof as there is comes largely from statistics and people do not understand, and therefore dislike, statistics. There are no human stories involved, there is no horror, nothing to warm our hearts or make us shudder. We read in the paper of the brave young mother whose life has been revolutionized by the installation of a vastly expensive home dialysis machine. Our hearts are warmed by the thoughts of the increased happiness that this machine has brought. We shudder a little at the terrible threat that this young woman's kidneys pose. We give thanks that the threat is not, at least this time, aimed at us. The machine may be expensive but the money is well spent.

Let us, for a moment, assume that someone discovers that kidney damage can be prevented by adding some item to our daily diet, perhaps seaweed. Would we get the same satisfaction from seeing our money spent on machinery for harvesting and processing the seaweed and on educating the public to eat it regularly? Which would we ourselves rather do, eat some unpalatable food every day in order to avoid kidney disease, or just give thanks that it was someone else who suffered? Whilst we are not faced with this particular choice, we are faced with a similar and yet much more basic one. Are we willing to take the responsibility for keeping our own and other people's bodies healthy, or are we just interested in providing a breakdown service?

The maxim 'prevention is better than cure' is an old one. No.one would dispute it, but how much effect does our belief in it have on our actions? Look back at the amount of money we spend on our health services and the way it is divided between prevention and cure. If we really believed the maxim, would we not divide it differently? We have got rid of a lot of the diseases of the past by preventing people from getting them. Some, such as diphtheria and smallpox, have been eliminated by immunization and vaccination. Others such as rickets have been controlled by improved diet. It is far cheaper to immunize all children against diphtheria than it was to keep fever hospitals open to treat children suffering from it − far less expensive in money and, much more important, in human suffering.

If our health service is to serve our health then we have to shift the balance of spending from cure to prevention. Once we can reduce the number of people getting ill we shall solve all the problems caused by the present shortage of hospital beds. But, important as it is, this is only one change that must be made if our health services really are to give us health instead of merely trying to repair the damage that we have done to ourselves.

The damage that we have done to ourselves! Yes, to a great extent we do damage our health ourselves. Let me repeat the opening sentences of this book. 'Man's worst enemy is himself. He breeds too rapidly. He eats too much. He pollutes his world. He squanders his resources.' If he does all this, and I shall add to the list of his misdemeanours, then can he expect to be healthy? I have already said that I consider our increasing population to be the greatest threat facing mankind and I shall deal with it at length in Chapter 15, so for the moment I'll leave it. 'He eats too much.' In our super-developed country malnutrition is rearing its head again, this time not because of lack of food but because we eat far too much of the wrong kind of food and because we refine the goodness out of our foods and then add synthetic vitamins, minerals, and flavouring to make up for what we have taken out. 'He pollutes his world.' Only now are we conscious of the damage we are doing to our environment. Food and pollution are so important that they each have a chapter to themselves later in the book. Finally 'he squanders his resources'. This will be dealt with under both pollution and population. For the moment I want to concentrate on man's attitude to his own health and to the health service.

Many of our present illnesses are self-induced. We eat, drink, and smoke too much and exercise too little. If, after a day in which we have given our bodies no vigorous exercise, we cannot sleep, then we rush to the doctor for sleeping tablets. We eat too much of the wrong kind of food and get obesity and digestive troubles. Our immediate reaction is to go to the doctor for slimming pills or an antacid. Smoking gives us a cough. Never mind, the doctor will oblige with a linctus. It would be sensible, but more difficult, to stop smoking, to take exercise, and to cut down on the foods we know to be harmful and/or fattening. It is so much easier to go to the doctor. After all, he is paid to take the responsibility. It is so much easier and pleasanter to swallow a pill than to change our habits.

Yes, the doctor is *paid* to take responsibility; he is *trained* to take responsibility, up to now he has usually been *willing* to take responsibility. But does it really make sense to use the skills of highly paid and highly trained people to treat discomforts we cause ourselves by our own foolishness? Will it not make better sense to stop using doctors as modern magicians or witch doctors able to wipe out our sins of sloth or gluttony with a prescription? This will give them time to get down to the vital job of trying to prevent disease and to detect early signs of it. We look on our doctors as gods, but we use them as glorified first-aid posts or as substitute confessionals.

A lot of the time of a good general practitioner is spent with the social and emotional problems of his patients. How much training does he get in psychiatry or social work? Will not this work be better done by other people who are specially trained for it? This will leave the doctor free for the job for which he has been so highly trained, and which only he can do, the detection and treatment of physical and mental illness. There is of course no hard and fast line to be drawn between physical, mental, social, and emotional stress; they are all very closely interwoven and there will always be overlap, but at least some of the burden can be lifted from the doctor's shoulders. The attachment of health visitors and district nurses to general practitioner groups is a welcome step in this direction.

Most important of all, however, is the need for us all to learn more about how our bodies work and how we must treat them in order to keep them healthy. This is the task of health educators working with all sections of the community. People should be able to estimate the risks involved in any particular habit and to decide for themselves whether the pleasure gained is worth the risk. Those who are trying to educate adults have a supremely difficult task; adults are set in their ways and loth to change. We who are concerned with children and young adults are more fortunate. It is true that they have acquired much questionable material from both precept and practice, but the mould has not set too hard and change is easier. We must also remember that they are at the age of revolt. Perhaps we can help them to revolt against some of the less healthy practices of their elders. This is already happening to some extent and we should be thankful that cannabis appears to be less harmful to health than either tobacco or alcohol. If we can help to bring about a healthier, more responsible generation we shall leave the doctors free to undertake regular checks and screening tests that will reduce the demand for the repair services.

The doctor too has a role to play in bringing this about. All too often he reaches for the prescription pad as the patient comes in through the door. All too seldom does he tell the patient why he is prescribing a particular drug and what effect it will probably have. Rarely does he tell the patient what the various possibilities of treatment are and let him help to decide how he will be treated. Even rarer is the doctor who will reveal his uncertainty to a patient, who will say 'I don't know' or 'I think it might be'. Doctors cannot be blamed for this, it is their patients who have forced the garment of omnipotence on them and who will grumble as they begin to shed it. We go to them expecting reassurance and 'something to make us feel better'. We do not want to be told to change our way of life, to eat less, or give up smoking or drinking. We do not want, although we may need, an explanation of our condition and its cause and treatment. We go to the doctor to be cured, by magic, in the form of a pill or potion.

Then there is time. Not only do we have our preconceived ideas about what doctors should do, but we keep them so busy that they have no time to do anything else. It is a vicious circle and, if it can be broken at all, it can only be broken through education.

Further Reading

Mallesen, Andrew. *Need Your Doctor be so Useless?* (London: Allen and Unwin, 1973.)

Gmur, B. O. *et al. Making Health Decisions.* (Prentice-Hall, 1970.)

3
Basic Rules of Health

It is easy to say that people should be responsible for maintaining their own health, but the fact that so few of us can measure up to the World Health Organization definition shows that it is not so easy to accomplish. Are there any basic rules that can help us? To simplify things let us look at the body's requirements for physical health; few of us can be really healthy mentally and socially if our bodies are not functioning properly. The body needs food, sleep, exercise, and fresh air, but how much and of what kind?

First of all, food. We read a lot about different diets and those of us who gain weight easily are only too familiar with the categories of food that we label carbohydrate, fat, and protein. We know that carbohydrates are starches and sugars which provide heat and energy for the body. Some people appear to metabolize their food less efficiently than others and seem to be able to eat to excess without putting on weight. Those of us who are less fortunate store it prudently away as subcutaneous, and usually very unwelcome, fat. We envy those who can eat cakes and sweets with impunity, but their impunity may only be apparent.

It is well-known that starch and sugar damage the teeth but this damage fades into insignificance when we look at what Captain Cleave has to say about the 'Saccharine Disease'.[1] If only a fraction of what he claims is true then it is time for us to sit up and take notice. Briefly his message is that though during the process of evolution any species adapts to changes in its environment, this adaptive process is a very, very slow one and if it is outstripped by environmental changes then things go wrong. Cleave claims that the adaptive processes of our digestive system have been outstripped by the refining of sugar and grain. This refining process greatly concentrates the substance and it removes the fibre from it. A diet rich in indigestible fibre results in the formation of bulky soft stools which pass rapidly through the gut. One consequence of a high fibre diet is that there is a reduction of bacterial colonization of the gut which affects bile and cholesterol metabolism. Also lower pressures are needed for propulsion and evacuation of the bowel contents, resulting in a lower incidence of varicose veins, haemorrhoids, and diverticulosis.

Both the concentration and the removal of fibre help to deceive our appetite and it becomes easy to take far more than the body needs. A child may well

[1] Cleave, Surgeon Captain T. C. *The Saccharine Disease*. John Wright and Sons Ltd., Bristol: 1974.

take more sugar on its breakfast cereal than it would get if it chewed sugar cane all day long. As well as removing bulk the absence of fibre means that we do less chewing of our food. In chewing we mix the food with saliva which both starts the digestive process and helps to fill the stomach. The high concentration of carbohydrate throws an unnatural strain on the pancreas, which produces insulin to help utilize the sugar, and if the pancreatic strain gets too much then diabetes might result. Any carbohydrate that is not burnt up by the body gets laid down as subcutaneous fat which leads to obesity. If nothing but natural whole-grain cereals were eaten and if refined sugars, brown as well as white, were avoided, then the appetite would be self-regulating and there would be no need for starvation diets. He quotes work done in Africa, India, and America which shows that diabetes, peptic ulcers, coronary thrombosis, gall stones, diverticulosis, varicose veins, and haemorrhoids are virtually non-existent amongst people eating unrefined food, whether it be sugar cane or sugar beet, maize or unpolished rice. But when these people change to a diet of refined foods, either because they move into urban areas or for other reasons, then within twenty years the incidence of all these conditions begins to increase alarmingly. There is an interesting graph showing the correlation between sugar consumption and death from diabetes, which illustrates the dramatic effect of sugar rationing during the two world wars (Figure 1). The fact that the death rate remained low when the sugar consumption increased after 1946 was due to the discovery of penicillin and the introduction of newer forms of insulin.

So far as peptic ulcers are concerned the suggestions of Cleave are revolutionary. A peptic ulcer is a break in the mucous membrane lining the

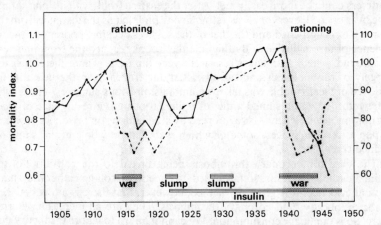

Figure 1   England and Wales diabetic mortality indices (1938 basis). (From Cleave, T. C. *The Saccharine Disease*. Bristol: J. Wright, 1974.) Broken line shows sugar consumption.

stomach and duodenum and results from either a defect of the mucous membrane or an alteration of the fluid contents, in particular an excess of acid. The conventional treatment has been frequent meals of a 'bland' variety so that (a) the stomach is not allowed to become empty of food – and so be at the mercy of the acid – and (b) there is nothing in the diet to irritate the delicate lining. Let me now quote Cleave who suggests that food acts as a buffer between the acid and the lining

> 'In this connection it should be added that it is now known that the highest acidities in the stomach occur during digestion and *not* in the empty resting state. Furthermore, the then distended wall of the stomach during digestion must operate against the mucosal defence, whereas the thick, non-distended wall in the resting state must operate in favour of that defence.
>
> It is not difficult to see how, under modern food processing, this reduction in buffering power very easily occurs. For the only component of food that buffers the acid is protein. Fats, starches and sugars do not affect the acid at all. And in the refining of carbohydrates the protein is either seriously reduced or removed altogether. A little later it will be shown, in fact, that there is a remarkable correlation throughout the world between the consumption of these 'protein-stripped' carbohydrates and the incidence of peptic ulcer.'[2]

He goes on to quote some fascinating evidence about the incidence of peptic ulcer in German troops during World War II. The incidence of ulcers was so high that special 'ulcer battalions' were formed so that the dietary needs of the sufferers could be more easily met. After the eastern front, with its long supply line, was opened, everyone was astounded to find that as the distance from the home base lengthened and the diet of the soldiers became 'poorer', so the incidence of ulcers declined. By the time the troops reached the front line near Stalingrad, where fear and stress were very high and where diet consisted largely of raw potatoes and turnips often dug frozen from the field, the incidence of ulcer trouble was nil, even amongst previous sufferers. Those who later returned and resumed a diet of refined foods got a resurgence of ulcer symptoms. This evidence is re-inforced by studies done on prisoners of war in Japan and other places, some of whom were fed on whole grain, some on refined cereals.

The case for coronary thrombosis being linked to the consumption of refined carbohydrates is, so far, based on general reasoning rather than hard factual evidence. It is generally agreed, however, that there is a link between diabetes, obesity, and coronary thrombosis. They are all increasing alarmingly. So is our sugar consumption. We cannot afford to ignore the theory put forward by Cleave that these apparently separate conditions are all aspects of

[2] Ibid.

one disease, 'The Saccharine Disease', and that the cause is simply our large consumption of refined sugar and starch. Yet this theory was first put forward in a book published in 1966[3] and very little notice was taken of it. Perhaps it is too simple for the technological age. But if the cause proves to be as simple as they suggest, the remedy will not be. Our present eating habits are very dear to us and a lot of big business is involved in making sure that they stay as they are. Cleave suggests that in time the body may adapt to these refined foods, but that meantime there is going to be a lot of suffering.

Cleave's hypothesis concerning the causation of the common diseases of western man has not yet gained wide acceptance, but a great deal of interest is now being shown and supporting evidence is coming in from many quarters.[4] It is possible that this is an idea whose hour has come. A more orthodox view is that fat, and in particular animal fat, contributes not only to the body surplus found in obesity, but also to that found lining major arteries and known as atheroma. In the coronary arteries the resultant narrowing may result in a heart attack. There is some evidence that modifying the type and quantity of fat consumed may reduce the incidence of heart attacks and angina. Certainly fat is the most concentrated source of calories available and therefore the most 'fattening' type of food, but it must be said that fried or any kind of fat cooked foods are digested very slowly and so help to stave off the pangs of hunger for longer than other types of food.

Protein is 'body-building', and unless eaten excessively it should not add greatly to our weight, although some protein foods are very high in calories. But protein in the form of meat, fish, cheese, and eggs can be very expensive. We can supplement our protein more cheaply by skimmed milk, soya flour, peas, beans, and nuts. Most dieticians urge weight watchers to eat a fairly high protein diet.

There are other substances which we need in our diet, and although we only need them in minute amounts we will not be healthy if our diet is deficient in them. These substances are vitamins and minerals. Unfortunately modern methods of refining and processing foods take out many of these vitamins and minerals. These refined foods then have synthetic vitamins and minerals added in an attempt to replace what has been taken out.

I believe that we suffer more than we realize by our modern eating habits. When a doctor attributed George Best's depression to a mineral deficiency we all laughed. But, since more and more people are suffering from depressions

---

[3] Cleave, T. C. and Campbell, G. D. *Diabetes, Coronary Thrombosis and the Saccharine Disease*. Bristol: John Wright, 1966.

[4] Heaton, K. W. 'Gallstone Formation', *Ninth Symposium on Advanced Medicine*, ed. G. Walker. London: Pitman Medical, 1973. Burkitt, D. P., A. R. P. Walker and N. S. Painter, 'Effect of Dietary Fibre on Stools and Transit Times and Its Role in the Causation of Disease'. *The Lancet*, 30 Dec. 1972. Heaton, K. W. and E. W. Pomare, 'Effect of Bran on Blood Lipids and Calcium'. *The Lancet*, 30 Dec. 1972.

and we don't seem to know why, can we afford to laugh? The crowning irony
is that those of us who want natural food such as whole-grain bread and
cereals and unpolished rice have to pay more for the fact that we don't want
them processed or added to. There are, however, many excellent books on
nutrition written by people with a greater knowledge of the subject than I
possess, and I mention a few at the end of the chapter. What I would ask is
that any class doing a health education course should study and discuss this
subject. To a large extent our bodies are what we eat.

> 'Oh sleep! It is a gentle thing
> Beloved from pole to pole'.[5]

Those who sleep well are indeed blessed. We all need sleep and the dreams
that accompany sleep. A sleepless night is looked on as something to be
dreaded and avoided at all costs. How much sleep do we need? There is no
hard and fast rule, we are all different with our own individual needs, but for
most of us the amount we require declines as we grow older. A new-born baby
sleeps about twenty hours out of the twenty-four, a grown man usually sleeps
about seven hours and it has been said that women require eight, but I think
that this is just a sexual myth. By the time we reach a really ripe old age we are
nodding off at all hours of the day and then wondering why we do not sleep
too well at night.

If we all need sleep, albeit in differing quantities, why is it that so many people have difficulty in sleeping? Many reasons can be given; anxiety, tension,
pain, and disturbance are some, but there is one that I think we do not stress
enough and that is lack of tiredness. By tiredness I mean physical tiredness.
There are very few manual workers visiting their doctors to ask for sleeping
tablets. Physical exhaustion is the best sleep inducer there is and we could
make much more use of it than we do. If we add fresh air to our energetic activity then a good night's sleep is doubly assured.

It is not, however, always possible, or desirable, for us to exhaust ourselves
physically before going to bed and we are all, at some time, going to lie in bed
unable to sleep. What do we do about it? We can, of course, take sleeping
tablets. Many people do, often with their doctor's blessing and possibly with
very good reason. Those who are in pain or who have just suffered some
anguish may need the aid of these powerful drugs. They should not be made to
feel guilty about this. But the rest of us often take pills just because we are
afraid of a wakeful night or afraid of being tired the next day. What alternatives are there? We can try to will ourselves to go to sleep but the more we
do this the wider awake we become. Worry kills sleep more quickly than
anything else and worrying about not sleeping is a sure means of keeping us
awake. Counting sheep, or stitches on an imaginary knitting needle, may
eventually work as a result of either exhaustion or boredom, but it is not

[5] *The Ancient Mariner* by S. T. Coleridge.

usually very effective. Relaxation is by far the best means. The sleeplessness may be due to tension, the relaxation of which will allow sleep to come. Even if it does not send us to sleep, relaxation can be almost as good as sleep. If our bodies are relaxed they are resting and will be refreshed by that rest. Relaxation, however, is something of a lost art and we may have to work at it. If we lie comfortably on the bed with our limbs supported and not cramped and first contract and then relax our muscles we can come to exert conscious control over them. It is often best to start with one set of muscles, say the arm, and work our way through all the muscles of the body tightening and relaxing each group in turn. When we have done this we can tighten them all together and then relax them all. The way we breathe can help. It has been said that the sigh is nature's way of relaxing and it is indeed difficult to sigh and tense your muscles at the same time. Sighing breaths, which can be silent, do help relaxation.

There is one thing to be said for being awake at night. Most of us complain that we have not enough time to think, or contemplate, or just day-dream. To lie awake at night when the world around you is asleep can be a luxury. Unless you are in pain or in a very uncomfortable bed you can lie in blissful quietude and either sort out your problems without the distractions of the daytime bustle, or you can just day-dream at night. You will not be tired the next day unless you expect to be and exhaust yourself with worrying about it. Dreamless sleep is often referred to as a great boon but recent research has shown that we need to dream as much as we need to sleep. An investigation of dreams, and why we dream, would make a fascinating subject for a class project; after all 'we are such stuff as dreams are made on, and our little life is rounded with a sleep'.[6]

Fresh air is something we take for granted. It has always been there and, until recently, we were sure that it always would be. There are people, but not many, who have an almost fanatical belief in the benefits of fresh air. They fling wide the windows, irrespective of the outside temperature, and take deep, almost gleeful breaths, whilst the other occupants of the room shiver and cower into corners away from the draught. For most of us fresh air indoors has become synonymous with a draught. We instal central heating and then protect it by all means at our disposal from the dreaded fresh air. Our doors are draught-proofed and our windows double-glazed. If we are ever foolhardy enough to open them, the air we let in may be anything but fresh. It is more likely to be laden with car exhaust fumes or, in the case of my house, with the stink of a nearby filthy river.

Fresh air is something we can no longer take for granted and it is by no means certain that it will always be with us. In Tokyo they already have coin-operated kiosks where you can go to buy a few breaths of oxygen. It has been suggested that the frequent yawning observable in many of our cities could be

---

[6] *The Tempest* by W. Shakespeare, Act 4, Scene I.

due to an excess of carbon monoxide. A science class might like to try measuring the amount of carbon monoxide in the air in the centre of some of our big cities. We need fresh air to remain healthy but it is no longer enough to tell people to open windows. We have to make sure that the air that comes in is fresh, but more of this in the chapter on pollution.

Exercise was something that our forbears did not usually need to worry about. Most of them were compelled to take far too much of it in the course of their daily work. But modern technology has changed all that and most of us never really exercise our bodies in the course of a normal work-day. We certainly get tired, but it is a different kind of tiredness from the physical exhaustion of our ancestors. Ours is probably a mixture of boredom, tension, anxiety, noise, poor diet, and possibly lack of pure air. Our bodies need exercise if they are to function properly and the exercise needs to be regular rather than violent. How many children take a bus to school when they could very well walk or cycle? How many adults use their cars for short journeys? Even some people with heart conditions are now told to take exercise. Why not get, or try to get, the class to walk to and from school for a month and to report on the benefits to their health as well as their saving of bus fares? The saved bus money could be used to buy sensible shoes in which to walk comfortably, but that is trespassing on the chapter in which feet are dealt with.

Our lack of regular and strenuous exercise may also be affecting our tempers. If you are feeling cross and frustrated and you have a huge pile of logs to chop in order to get a fire going, you can get rid of your bad temper and frustration as you chop the wood and then sit down serenely to enjoy the fire. Switching on an electric fire or even striking a match to light a gas fire gets rid of nothing, so the temper and frustration must find other outlets. These outlets may be other people or other people's property. It is a sobering thought that violence and vandalism may, in part, arise from a lack of wood to chop. Get your pupils to try some form of violent physical exercise next time they are seething with temper or frustration. The resultant essays and discussion might surprise you, and them.

Further Reading

Birds Eye Ltd. *Basic Nutrition* (four teaching programmes and teacher's manual). (Oxford: Pergamon Press Ltd.).

Ministry of Agriculture, Fisheries and Food. *Manual of Nutrition.* (London: H.M.S.O., 1970).

Cleave, Surgeon Captain T. C. *The Saccharine Disease.* (Bristol: J. Wright, 1974).

Gmur, B. O. *et al. Making Health Decisions.* (London: Prentice Hall, 1970).

4
The Human Support System

The last chapter dealt with the basic physical needs of the body but there are many other things on which we are almost equally dependent. In looking at these things which I shall call supports, I also want to consider this support system as a general basis for health education. It is so easy for health education to become anti-life; to become a doctrine of 'Thou Shalt Not'.

Thou shalt not smoke. Smoking may give you chronic bronchitis or cancer of the lung.

Thou shalt not drink. Alcohol may lead to cirrhosis of the liver, brain damage, or even alcoholism.

Thou shalt not over-eat. Over-eating may lead to obesity which may in turn lead to coronary thrombosis.

Thou shalt not indulge in sexual activities. Intercourse may result in venereal disease or help to bring an unwanted child into the world.

How long will it be before we find 'thou shalt not live, it is too dangerous'? Or at least get to the stage where, in the words of the old song:

> 'If it's something you enjoy you can be certain that
> It's illegal, it's immoral, or it makes you fat'.

As health educators in school it is our duty to make young people aware of the dangers that may arise from certain acts or behaviour. At the same time we must remember that we are educating them towards the attainment of a state of complete physical, mental, and social well-being. We are not trying to replace the religious hell of fire and brimstone by an ill-health hell of coronaries and venereal disease. Education for health is not and must never be synonymous with anti-life education.

If we are to warn people of the dangers yet avoid telling them what they must not do, then we must look at some of the reasons why people indulge in things which they know are harmful. One reason is that they satisfy a real, imagined, or created need, so perhaps we should start by looking at human needs.

For survival we all need the three basic elements – air, fire, and water. Without them we could not live, but we must also realize that given too much of them we could not live either. Too much oxygen is just as disastrous for the human body as too little and, whilst we could not live without the warmth of the sun's fire, even a little more would turn us into cinders. A few hours without a drink is sufficient to convince us of our need for water but the mere idea of too much water in the wrong place is enough to terrify us all. We must accept, therefore, that whilst we have basic needs for certain things, we also need to have these things in fairly limited amounts. Too much of anything is as bad as too little. All life is, however, dependent on the presence of certain factors which are essential for its support and which could be said to form its 'support system'. Simple forms of life have simple support systems. The support system of any organism as complex as the human body is bound to be very complicated. When we come to present-day civilized man, the complexity and variety of support is infinite.

Our support systems grow as we grow. A new-born baby has a relatively simple support system, in other words his needs are few, although not necessarily easy to satisfy. Apart from his basic physical need of air, warmth, and food he needs only the security and comfort of his mother. He needs to feel the close contact of her body, to hear the sound of her voice and to experience the general feeling of nearness. If, at this stage, there were no father or other family it would affect the new-born child only insofar as it affected the mother. As the baby grows, however, so do his needs and he begins to reach out to, and to interact with, the father and other members of the nuclear family. The environment too becomes of increasing importance, and it is now thought that from a very early age he is mentally stimulated by his surroundings. He discovers his own body and the sexual pleasure he can get by handling his genitals. He explores an ever-increasing environment as he becomes more mobile. Toys and other material objects enter his world and are all absorbed into his support system. We have all seen a small child hungry and crying for food, but kept happy for a time by a cuddle or a favourite toy, perhaps whilst mother prepares his food. He is, temporarily, replacing the support of food by that of a cuddle or a toy. In other words, mental or emotional satisfaction is being accepted as a substitute for physical satisfaction. His support system is widening.

It will go on widening as he extends the boundaries of his experience. The number and kind of things that become an integral part of his support system will depend partly on his genetic inheritance but even more on his environment. No one can include in his support system things which are outside his experience. This does not exclude fantasy, but we can only conjure up visions of things that have in some form or other impinged on our imagination. It follows, therefore, that a child from a rich and stimulating environment will have a richer, wider support system and will be able to choose, at least to a certain extent, which supports he will lean on. This could be another handicap for the deprived child and could run parallel to that suggested by Bernstein's studies on language development.

Let us look at the support system of a mature cultured human being. We

must, of course, start with the basic physical needs – air, food, and warmth–
but now we must add comfort, sex, the feeling of power derived from driving
cars, relationships (both within and without the family), food (as an emotional
rather than a physical satisfaction), religion, music, reading, role-playing (off
the stage), intellectualism, gardening, walking, athletics, sport, drugs
(including alcohol and nicotine), clothes, status symbols, job satisfaction,
money etc. etc. It could be an endless list. None of the things on it is bad in
itself but any one of them in excess can be harmful.

If we look at our own support systems we shall notice several things about
them. The most obvious thing is that we did not sit down with a list and choose
rationally the supports that we thought the most sensible or desirable for us.
Some of them developed in response to basic physical or emotional needs.
Into this category we must put food (in its role of provider of the body's
needs), warmth, and personal relationships. Everyone needs these things.
Others came because of social customs and pressures. Very few, if any, of our
supports are adopted as a result of a rational choice; consequently most support systems are haphazard, unbalanced affairs.

Those of us who have acquired wide support systems are fortunate indeed.
If we are deprived of one support we have a variety of others on which we can
fall back. People with narrow systems are in trouble when they lose one of
their supports. As our grandmothers used to tell us, we should not put all our
eggs in one basket. This is just what happens to a heroin addict; he becomes
over-dependent on one support. Also some supports become harmful more
easily than others and we would do well to look at our own systems in this
light. Before we can teach others we need to examine ourselves, to see where
our systems are narrow, unbalanced or harmful, and to adjust them if possible
but, if not, at least to see them as they are. It is the old story of removing the
beam from our own eye before worrying about the mote in someone else's.
One headmaster said that although he did not really like alcohol he did not
have the courage to refuse a drink at a party, yet he expected his sixteen-year
old daughter to refuse cannabis at the parties she attended. He at least was
aware of his own dependence on conformity.

Anyone who has taken the above sermon seriously enough to examine his
or her own support system honestly is probably feeling rather worried. The
best of us have unbalanced support systems which include harmful 'props'.
What can we do about it? Suicide seems a trifle dramatic, but a complete
reformation with the idea of transforming ourselves into beings with perfectly
balanced, harmless systems is quite beyond most of us. It is perhaps as well
that perfection is beyond our grasp, because if we attained it we would cease
to be human and humanity is an essential quality in any educator, particularly
a health educator. We have to start by accepting ourselves as we are. This is .
the most difficult job that any of us ever tackles, but we must try to accomplish it if we are to help young people first to discover their identity and
then to accept it. That is not to suggest that we sit back smugly thinking that,

since we cannot perfect our systems, we might as well leave them as they are. If we do that we will first stagnate and then start to regress, for nothing stands still. We must continue to strive for a better balance, which is only another way of saying that we continue to mature and grow wiser. Our conscious efforts to improve, however marginally, our own support systems will help us to understand the young people we are trying to help.

Having been brave enough to examine our own support systems we can now ask the pupils to examine theirs. An outline of what they believe to be their own support system might make an unusual and valuable piece of homework. It could be followed by asking the pupils to outline what they believe to be the support system of one of their friends in the class. A comparison of the supports they think they depend on with the supports that their friends think they depend on might give rise to some surprises.

Another interesting exercise would be to get them to try to classify some of the supports according to the type of need they appear to meet. This will not be easy and some will have to be put in more than one category.

Food is one example of this; as a nutrient it fulfils a physical need, but as I shall show in the next chapter it also has psychological and social functions. By encouraging the pupils to think in this way we would improve their understanding of themselves and at the same time lay the foundation for future lessons. If, for example, we look at smoking as a support, we can weigh up its advantages and its disadvantages and investigate the reasons why people smoke as well as the effects of smoking. In other words we can study the phenomenon of human beings smoking tobacco with at least some degree of objectivity, and we can try to help them not only to get enough information but to think about it, so that if they then decide to start to smoke or to continue smoking they are not doing so in ignorance. Apart from the fact that we have no right to tell them what they should, or should not, do outside school, we know that 'telling' will be ineffective. They are going to make up their own minds. All that we can do is to try to get them to think before they do so.

Further Reading

Campbell, J. C. *The Pleasure Areas.* (London: Eyre and Methuen, 1973.)

5
Food

Food is one of the basic necessities of the body. It is, in this form, a universal support. Furthermore we need it in fairly set amounts. Too much can be almost as harmful as too little.

If we are to achieve, or maintain, physical and mental health, we must eat an adequate diet. I include mental as well as physical health because I subscribe wholeheartedly to the doctrine that 'the secret of happiness is a good digestion'. Fifty years ago all our ill-health was attributed to physical causes; then the psychosomatic diseases were 'discovered' and we all began to look for mental or emotional causes for our physical ailments. The discovery that mental or emotional upset could disturb the physical functioning of the body was a great step forward, but, as usual, the pendulum swung too far. Suddenly everyone began searching for psychological or emotional causes for everything and it became difficult to sneeze, in certain 'enlightened' circles, without someone starting a little amateur psycho-analysis to find the underlying emotional stress that had caused it. Now the pendulum is swinging back again and we can only hope that this time it will stop mid-way. It has been discovered that phenylketonuria, which can give rise to mental deficiency, is due to an inability to digest certain protein, and it can be prevented from causing brain damage if it is discovered early enough and the child is taken off milk. Similar physical abnormalities are being investigated as a possible cause of schizophrenia. And let us not forget the doctor who recently attributed George Best's depression to a lack of a certain mineral salt.

We have looked at the constituents of an ideal diet and its nutritive importance, but now it is food as a psychological support, I could almost say as an 'addictive substance', that I want to look at. In his stages of development Freud includes, in fact starts with, the stage of oral satisfaction. The young baby gets most of its pleasure and its learning, as well as its sustenance, through its mouth. A frightened as well as a hungry child can be comforted by being given its mother's breast to suck. We used to quieten babies by giving them dummies which were, significantly, called comforters. Many children suck their thumbs, a piece of blanket or anything that comes to hand to console themselves in time of stress. Young children also put things to their mouths as part of their learning process, but here we are only concerned with the mouth as a source of physical or emotional satisfaction.

Sucking as a source of satisfaction is obviously a primitive instinct essential to the physical and psychological survival of the child. For many of us it is an instinct that we never outgrow. It is an instinct reinforced in many ways by the customs of our present society. If a child falls, hurts itself, and cries, it is common practice to comfort it by giving it a sweet to suck. Even our Child Welfare Clinics used to give chocolate drops to children who were being immunized. This way of encouraging, perhaps even bribing, children to be good and quiet continues throughout childhood. It is the easy road to peace. We must either investigate and try to remove the cause of the child's grief or pop a sweet into its mouth. The causes of children's tears can be so obscure, cuddles are time-consuming and not always effective, but sweets are so easy to give and work so well. Is it any wonder that our children grow up as compulsive sweet-eaters? Is it so surprising that grown men and women like to suck sweets or the ends of pipes or cigarettes? Were we all weaned too soon, or just not allowed by our civilization to get beyond our need for oral satisfaction? Whatever the cause the results are disastrous.

Why are so many people overweight? In some cases it is due to sheer ignorance of the causes of obesity. It is possible that in these cases the giving of knowledge about the need for a balanced diet and the effect on the body of various kinds of food, *might* help. There are, however, many other cases of people with a good knowledge of nutrition and food values who are still overweight. In these cases knowledge is not enough. Most of them are aware of their condition and are worried by it. They know that they run a much greater risk of ill-health or early death than do their slim companions: they have the terrible burden of carrying all this surplus weight around with them. And it is a burden; only those who are fat or who have been fat can really appreciate this. They know how Christian, in Pilgrim's Progress, must have felt carrying his burden on his back. They know that they have to pay more for less exciting clothes. They know that they are slow and clumsy, that neither glamour nor elegance can ever be theirs and – their feet ache! They also know that all these things could be remedied by correct eating. Yet many of them remain fat. Why?

Many of them are, as I myself was, compulsive eaters. It is so easy to react to the stresses and strains of life by eating. Eating, or sucking a sweet, serves the same purpose as the dummy or the childhood sweet that stopped us crying; it comforts us. Furthermore, it is easy to react in this way without being aware of it. I had reacted to stress or extra work by over-eating for twenty years without realizing it. Even when the idea first occurred to me I refused to accept it; but it is only since accepting it that I have been able to do anything about it. Ingrained habits are difficult things to change and giving up comfort-eating is just as difficult as giving up smoking or any other addiction.

Let us look for a moment at the 'mores' of the society that produces so many people who eat too much. And we must remember that these are not just fat people. Some thin people seem to eat to excess but their metabolism is inefficient, allowing them to do so without putting on weight. Eating is more than just a way of nourishing our bodies. It is a social habit. For years now people have been jokingly saying that we shall soon be able to give up food altogether and replace it by tablets; the prospect fills most of us with horror. Why? We grumble about the amount of time and money spent on meal preparation and we grumble even more about washing up and clearing away after a meal. Surely we ought to welcome the prospect of our release from all these chores. Why do we not? This is partly because cooking is one of the few creative arts still practised regularly and, although the creativity involved in frying fish fingers is limited, most of us get a certain satisfaction from meal preparation. Then there is the question of what we would do with the time if we did not use it preparing meals. It is true that we always seem to be busy, that we never have the time to do all the things we want to do, but is our busyness any more than seeming? With mechanization and shorter working hours few of us spend as much time or energy on our work as our forbears did. The old trade unionist's dream of eight hours work, eight hours sleep, and eight hours play has been more than realized. Things have gone so far that we are now 'educating for leisure' and the threat of boredom hangs over us all. Perhaps subconsciously, if not consciously, we realize that meal preparation is one satisfying way of keeping boredom at bay.

But is that the only reason why we reject the idea of tablets instead of meals? Of course not. Meals satisfy much more than hunger. They appeal to many of our senses. It has been said that we eat with our eyes as well as with our mouth, and we should not underestimate the roles played by colour and shape in making food attractive. Even more important is smell. We have all been stimulated and delighted, or revolted, by food smells. The texture of foods can also give us pleasure – crisp crusts or apples, tender meat, the soft melting texture of creamed potatoes. But of course the proof of the pudding is in the eating and the supreme pleasure comes from the taste.

All these are very good arguments for food as opposed to tablets, but they are only part of the story. Meals eaten alone may look, smell, and taste superb but they are never as satisfying as food eaten in good company. Meals are social occasions. They may be the only time when all the family sits down together without newspapers, television, or other similar distractions. So food becomes linked with talk, with reaching out to other people, getting to know them, giving and receiving sympathy. If this is true of everyday family meals, it is even more true of social occasions. We want to make a friendly gesture so we invite someone in for a meal. Even if a visitor drops in unexpectedly we almost automatically set about making them feel welcome by offering them food and/or drink. It is virtually an extension of our proffered hand, a means of expressing affection and good wishes. In our culture we are shy of making overt expressions of affection; we find it easier to convey warmth of feeling through the medium of food and drink. This type of hospitality is ancient, stemming from a willingness to share that is entirely laudable. In our present affluent society, however, it can take on more sinister overtones.

One of these is 'keeping up with' or 'going one better than' the Joneses.

How much modern entertaining contains at least an element of competitiveness? Then there is the effect the hospitable offering might have on the recipient. This could range from indigestion through an unwanted weight gain to the tragedy of a road accident caused by alcoholic intoxication. Often our desire to express affection is directed towards children with sweets as the medium.

Almost all grandmothers like to give sweets or to cook special cakes or puddings for their grandchildren. The intention is benevolent but the results—the development of a 'sweet tooth', dental caries, obesity and a lack of essential nutrients—can be malignant.

Must we offer food and drink in this way? I think we must, it is such an integral part of our culture. We can, however, give a little more thought to what we offer. Grandparents can offer fruits or small toys and the rest of us too can give thought to the effect our offering is going to have on the recipient. That is where we, as health educators, come in. Our role here is the same as with all addictions; it is firstly to acquire and disseminate knowledge and secondly to help to change the climate of opinion. For example, since the introduction of the breathalyser tests, it has become easier to refuse an extra drink by pleading that you have to drive. Refusing alcohol on these grounds has become socially acceptable and hosts are no longer affronted by such refusals.

We must make it equally socially acceptable for the dieter to refuse a piece of cake without giving offence. Of course, there would be less need for these refusals if we could get people to give more thought to the type of food they offer. Is there less affection in a salad than in a plate of chips?

Get the class to compile menus that they themselves have either been offered or have offered to other people. Examine these from a health standpoint and discuss ways in which they could have been made healthier. Discussion groups on why young people spend so much time chewing would be interesting. How often do they eat when they are not hungry, and why? How many are conscious of indulging in comfort-eating? Is there any connection between this and whether or not they were breast-fed or the age at which they were weaned? Do they think we should try to change the social climate where eating is concerned? If so, how would they suggest we do it?

Let us be under no illusion, trying to change people's eating habits will be one of our most difficult jobs. How many millers, bakers, restaurants, confectioners, and advertisements are busy pandering to our most gluttonous tastes? But if we look at the results of unwise eating, both in the form of malnutrition and of obesity, we can be in no doubt about the necessity for trying to do it. Even simple obesity carries an increased risk of heart disease, as well as diabetes. These are among our greatest killers. Let us fight them on our tea tables.

Further Reading

Burnett, John. *Plenty and Want*. (London: Pelican, 1966.)

6
Tobacco

Smoking has been with us since the sixteenth century, and ever since its introduction it has had its advocates and its opponents. As it is only recently that scientific evidence of its ill-effects upon health has been produced, we must assume that before this the opposition was based on other factors. The two obvious objections are financial and aesthetic. If we spend more of our income than we can afford on tobacco then we shall either suffer ourselves or make our families suffer. As usual it is the poor who are in danger here; people with high incomes can afford to smoke heavily without their families suffering from malnutrition. The aesthetic effects are more evenly distributed, although here again the poor, living in cramped, overcrowded conditions, are at a disadvantage. How valid are the aesthetic objections to smoking?

The answer, of course, depends partly on whether the question is asked of a smoker or a non-smoker. When I smoked forty cigarettes a day, a smoke-filled room did not worry me at all. Now, after seven and a half years as a non-smoker, I find it very objectionable. How much right have non-smokers to object to the pollution of the air they breathe? I think that most reasonable-minded smokers would agree that public places should be free of this pollution. Non-smoking accommodation on trains and in places of public entertainment has been extended; perhaps soon smoking on the upper-decks of short-distance buses will be stopped. After all, there are more seats on the upper-deck and non-smokers are often forced upstairs by lack of room and almost suffocated by the atmosphere they meet. Children always want to ride on the tops of buses. Do we want our children choked with smoke?

Extensions of no-smoking zones are desirable, but have we any right to ask people to give up smoking altogether, or, in the case of children, to 'stop them starting'? Even more pertinent, if we decide we have a 'right' to ask, would asking be effective? Those who would argue that we have such a right would quote some of the alarming figures about the effect of smoking on health that are now available. The opposition would say that a person's health is his own concern and is nobody else's business. Which, if either, of these viewpoints is right?

John Stuart Mill tells us that the only warrants society has for interfering 'individually or collectively with the liberty of action of any of their number are self-protection. ... His own good, either physical or moral, is not sufficient warrant'. He goes on to tell us that we may remonstrate with, entreat or persuade him, but we have no grounds for 'compelling him or visiting him with any evil' if he continues in his action. (We must remember John Stuart Mill when we consider illegal drugs.) In the case of smoking, a person who continues in the habit will cause enough 'evil' to visit himself; there is no need for society to add to his punishment. It is, however, possible for us to try to change the climate of social opinion without going as far as James I of England (VI of Scotland), who condemned smoking as 'a branch of the sin of drunkenness which is the root of all sins'. A start has already been made in changing society's mind. People are beginning to feel furtive and ashamed when they smoke and it is more difficult to find ash trays both in private houses and public places. How far do we want this to go? In view of the great danger to health it must surely be a good thing for smoking to become less acceptable socially, but we do not want to drive it underground. Perhaps there is little danger of this whilst the tobacco companies are spending well over fifty *million* pounds per year in sales promotion. Even John Stuart Mill would agree that for self-protection society needs to stop this. But how can society stop it when governments rely on the revenue they get from cigarettes? A former minister in a Conservative government, once Minister of Health, wrote in 1966: 'Smokers, mainly cigarette smokers, contribute some one thousand million pounds yearly to the Exchequer . . . and no-one knows better than the Government that they simply can't afford to lose so much.' In 1969, in a reply to a letter from a colleague, a Labour minister expounded this view in greater detail. He wrote:

'The introduction of a meaningful differential tax on cigarettes would be bound to have a seriously detrimental effect on the total revenue obtainable from tobacco. The object of such a tax would be to reduce cigarette smoking, and pipes and cigars would not be acceptable alternatives for many cigarette smokers. Furthermore, apart from those who gave up smoking altogether, cigarette smokers who switched to cigars would consume less tobacco in proportion to their expenditure and those who switched to pipe tobacco would consume less tobacco in proportion to the time spent in smoking. Thus the capacity of the tobacco duty to produce revenue would be eroded.'[1]

As the tape *Up in Smoke* produced by ASH[2] tells us, without the revenue from tobacco the government would not be able to afford nuclear weapons.

Let us now look at some of the facts about the effect of smoking on health contained in the recent report of the Royal College of Physicians, *Smoking and Health Now*.

[1] From *Smoking and Health Now*, Report of the Royal College of Physicians, 1971.
[2] ASH, *Up in Smoke*, Royal College of Physicians, 11 St Andrew's Place, Regent's Park, NW1 4LB.

1. Every year lung cancer kills over four times as many people as do road accidents.
2. Cigarette smokers are about twice as likely to die in middle age as are non-smokers. (See Figure 2 and Table 1.)
3. If present smoking habits continue it is estimated that in twenty years time there will be fifty thousand annual deaths from lung cancer in this country. If cigarette smoking were to cease, the number would be less than five thousand.
4. In 1968, 31 per cent of deaths of men between thirty-five years and sixty-four years of age were due to coronary thrombosis.
5. The risk of younger age groups dying from coronary thrombosis is two or three times greater in smokers than in non-smokers.

Table 1 Life expectancy of American men at various ages, and 'years of life lost' by cigarette smokers[1]

Cigarettes per day	Life Expectation	Present age								
		25	30	35	40	45	50	55	60	65
0	Years expected	48·6	43·9	39·2	34·5	30·0	25·6	21·4	17·6	14·1
1–9	Years expected	44·0	39·3	34·7	30·2	25·9	21·8	17·9	14·5	11·3
	Years lost[2]	4·6	4·6	4·5	4·3	4·1	3·8	3·5	3·1	2·8
10–19	Years	43·1	38·4	33·8	29·3	25·0	21·0	17·4	14·1	11·2
	Years lost[2]	5·5	5·5	5·4	5·2	5·0	4·6	4·0	3·5	2·9
20–39	Years expected	42·4	37·8	33·2	28·7	24·4	20·5	17·0	13·7	11·0
	Years lost[2]	6·2	6·1	6·0	5·8	5·6	5·1	4·4	3·9	3·1

[1] (From Royal College of Physicians, *Smoking and Health Now*. London: Pitmans, 1971.)
[2] The decrease in the number of years of life lost by cigarette smokers as they get older (which may suggest that their outlook improves as they continue to smoke) is, of course, due to the shortening expectation of life. The *percentage* reduction of expectation of life gets greater with advancing age. Thus the smoker of 10–19 cigarettes per day has an expectation reduced by 11 per cent when he is 25, but by 21 per cent when he is 65.

The National Child Development Study of the National Children's Bureau has published, among other statistics, figures that compare the differences in height and in reading age between the children of mothers who smoked after the fourth month of pregnancy and those who did not. The children of the mothers who smoked were, on average, 1 cm shorter in height and four months behind in their reading age compared to the children of the non-smokers, both at seven years of age and at *eleven years* of age. When this long-term effect is added to the information we already have that the children of mothers who

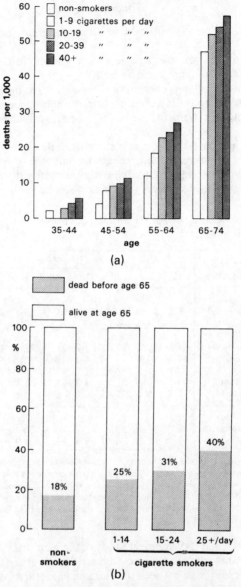

Figure 2 (a) Number of deaths each year per thousand in American men at various ages according to numbers of cigarettes smoked. Death-rates naturally increase with age. Smoking causes a greater proportionate increase in annual death-rates in younger than in older men, but the risk of smoking is really more serious in the older men because their death rates are so much higher. It is more dangerous nearly to double a large risk than to raise a small risk nearly threefold. The heavier smokers have a

(contd.)

smoke are likely to be smaller and less mature and to have a higher perinatal mortality than those of non-smoking mothers, then we have a good case against smoking in pregnancy.

The list of risks of early death, or worse still disablement, could be endless. A great deal of publicity has been given to these facts and yet people continue to smoke. Why? Part of the answer is contained in the quotations from government ministers. Smoking has official government support and people still believe that the government would not allow them to run such terrible risks, so they ignore the evidence. But they also ignore it because they want to ignore it. All the reasons given for compulsive over-eating apply here. Man is in desperate need of comfort and security. He is even willing to put his life at risk in the search for it. Also, nicotine is *very* addictive.

What can health educators do about it? They can disseminate the facts, and this they must do. There is, however, no point in telling people not to smoke. It must be an individual decision. Once again we are back to individual support systems. Smoking is a support. Is it the best available for any individual or could a safer alternative be found? Our job is to get people to examine their reasons for smoking, or for wanting to start smoking; to look at the expense and dangers involved; to examine other supports that might be available as alternatives, and to make their own choice. As citizens we should also look at the position of our government and ask ourselves if it is a position we feel able to support.

I have quoted very few statistics about the effects of smoking because they are all set out with admirable clarity in *Smoking and Health Now,* a report of the Royal College of Physicians. It is an eminently readable report which only costs 50p. Any teacher dealing with the subject should possess and have read this book. It contains all the facts and figures about the effects of smoking. Together with *The Young Smoker* by John M. Bynner (see Further Reading), which examines the reasons why children start to smoke, it will give the

---

Figure 2 (*contd.*)

risk of dying each year which is similar to that of non-smokers ten years older. There were too few deaths in smokers of 1–9 cigarettes per day aged 35–44 to provide a reliable figure; (b) Proportion of men aged 35 who will die before they reach the age of 65 according to their smoking habits. These figures show the chances a man aged 35 has of dying before the age of 65 if he is either a non-smoker or smokes various numbers of cigarettes. Only 18 per cent of the non-smokers but 25 per cent of the lighter smokers, and 31 per cent of the moderate smokers and 40 per cent of the heavier smokers (2 in 5) will die before they are 65. Of those who do reach this age more of the smokers than of the non-smokers are already disabled by chronic disease of the heart or lungs and the years of retirement will be fewer for the smokers than for the non-smokers. The chances of the lighter smokers may be better than those shown because this group probably includes some formerly heavy smokers who have reduced their smoking due to illness. (From Royal College of Physicians. *Smoking and Health Now.* Pitmans, 1971.)

teacher background knowledge and the confidence needed to face questions from pupils.

The tobacco companies spend 50 million pounds a year in sales promotion. How do they spend it, and why? Get the pupils to examine cigarette advertisements. Whom are they designed to attract? What emotions do they appeal to? What effect do coupons have on sales? Should cigarette companies be allowed to sponsor sports events, thus giving the impression of a link between sport (and health) and smoking? Does the Government Health Warning on cigarette packets have any effect? Why do people start smoking? Why do they continue to smoke? How much does group pressure affect smoking habits? The list of topics for discussion and investigation could go on for ever. Each class should be able to find something of interest. Will the newly published tar and nicotine content tables change people's smoking habits?

For older pupils it might be valuable, and it will certainly be fun, to play a tape or record of part of 'The Best of Bob Newhart' in which he does a 'send-up' of the discovery of tobacco. It might help to provide a completely new way of looking at smoking. The weapon it uses is laughter and that is a weapon we could make much more use of.

Further Reading

Bynner, J. M. *The Young Smoker.* (London: H.M.S.O., 1969.)
Royal College of Physicians. *Smoking and Health Now.* (London: Pitmans, 1971.)
Smoking and Health. Dept. of Education and Science, Elizabeth House, York Road, London, SE1, 1971.

7
Alcohol

The alchemists who first distilled alcohol in the west called it *aqua vitae*, water of life. The euphoria that it produced was taken for an intensification of life itself. It was hailed as the sovereign remedy for many ills and was widely used. Here is an early claim made on its behalf:

'It sloweth age, it strentheneth youth; it helpeth digestion; it cutteth flegme; it abandoneth melancholie; it relisheth the heart; it lighteneth the mind; it quickeneth the spirits; it strengtheneth the hydropsie; it healeth the strangurie; it pounceth the stone; it expelleth the gravel; it puffeth away ventositie; it keepeth and preserveth the head from whirling, the eyes from dazzling, the tong from lisping, the mouth from snaffling, the teeth from chattering, and the throat from rattling; it keepeth the weason from stiffling, the stomach from wambling, and the heart from swelling; it keepeth the hands from shivering, the sinews from shrinking, the weins from crumbling, the bones from aching and the marrow from soaking'.[1]

As J. C. Furnas says, nobody wants his weason to stiffle or his stomach to wamble unnecessarily, so the popularity of alcohol was enhanced by such advice.

In the early days drinking was condoned, even accepted, by all religions including the Quakers, but as the evils of over-indulgence became more and more evident pleas were made for temperance. The pleas for temperance soon turned into calls for abstinence and the extravagant claims made for the benefits of alcohol were soon being matched by diatribes against it. In 1811 Dr Nathaniel Prime of Long Island was saying:

'No better fuel can you afford the lusts of the flesh than ardent spirits − drunkeness and lewdness go hand in hand . . . few who have drunk a gill of ardent spirits can be exposed to . . . small temptation without becoming adulterers in the sight of God . . .'

And next year the Rev. Herman Humphrey, virtual founder of Amherst College, writes:

Intemperate drinking is the highway to perdition . . . a fiery stream which

[1] Furmas, J. C. *The Late Demon Rum*. London: W. H. Allen, 1965.

empties into the bottomless pit. All who embark on this flood are in danger of hell fire.[2]

These two gentlemen are only attacking spirits, ardent spirits, and intemperate drinking, but soon wines and beer were also under attack and the following parody of the witches of Macbeth is a fitting reply to the eulogy on alcohol quoted above:

> 'Round about the cauldron go,
> In the poisoned entrails throw.
> Drugs that in the coldest veins
> Shoot incessant fiery pains;
> Herbs that brought from Hell's back door,
> Do its business slow and sure . . .
> Dropsies, agues, fierce catarrhs,
> Pestilential inward wars,
> Fevers, gouts, convulsive starts,
> Racking spasms in vital parts,
> And men shall call the liquor good,
> The more with death it thicks the blood . . .'[2]

The wheel has come round full circle, aquae-vitae now thicks the blood with death.

In the United States of America the so-called temperance movement soon came to look on temperate drinkers as 'wicked triflers with evil'. A moderate drinker was considered worse than a sot because he 'showed that a man might use liquor and yet not beat his wife, wreck his home, defraud his creditors, destroy himself body and soul, and fill a drunkard's grave'. The call was for total abstinence and since it was obvious that there was no chance of voluntary abstinence the aid of the law was sought. First there were local laws forbidding the sale of alcohol, then state laws and finally in 1920 total prohibition throughout the whole of the United States of America. The prohibition movement was doomed to failure from the start. The consumption of alcohol had been far too widespread and the fact that if it was drunk in moderation it caused little harm was far too widely known. As someone said, if it was a poison it was a mighty slow one, so many regular drinkers lived to a healthy old age. No law can be expected to work if it is in opposition to what the majority of the people call common sense.

The fact that we have not progressed very far since the days of prohibition is obvious if we look at the reactions to the taking of the drugs that are illegal today. We still get the same euphoric praise and the same shrill denunciations, and we are still trying to gain control by prohibition. But alcohol has been with us for a long time and we know quite a lot about it and about its effects, so we should be able to examine some of that knowledge. Here are some facts taken from *Teaching About Alcohol* by Frances Todd (see Further Reading):

[2] Ibid.

eulogy – a speech or writing in praise

'The use – and misuse – of ethyl alcohol as a beverage predates civilization. Just as people throughout the world eat the kind of food they can readily grow, so they make alcoholic beverages, by fermentation or distillation, from locally grown plants which contain sugar or starch. The alcoholic content differs widely between beverages.

Beer, wine, and distilled liquors all contain many substances other than alcohol. Any palatable alcoholic beverage, even if taken undiluted, is at least half water. Most drinks contain congeners which add flavor and color.

Both by definition and by its use and effects on the body, alcohol may be properly called a food and a drug. It is, however, a very poor food from a nutritional standpoint even though it is a rich source of energy and hence of calories.'

'Alcohol, though a very inadequate food, is a rich source of fuel. Less than ten per cent of the alcohol consumed leaves the body through the breath and urine. The other ninety per cent is absorbed into the blood from the stomach and small intestines, is transported to the liver, and then circulates throughout the body via the arteries, capillaries, and veins.

The liver is the only organ able to initiate the process by which the body disposes of alcohol. The liver works steadily as long as any alcohol is present, but even the healthiest liver cannot cope with more than two or three drops of it at one time. Excessive alcohol cannot be stored and so continues to travel in the blood while it waits its turn in the liver's chemical laboratory.

Each individual disposes of alcohol at a unique and constant rate. The average person can oxidize the alcohol in one ordinary high-ball in about an hour. Nothing is known which will significantly hasten oxidation, but much is known about factors which may slow down the absorption of alcohol to a rate compatible with the oxidative capacity of the liver. If absorption is delayed until the liver can dispose of alcohol, even its mildest effects will not be apparent.

To a great extent, a knowledgeable drinker can prevent or minimize the sedative and anaesthetic effects of alcohol. If he limits his drinking to one or two well-diluted drinks, sips them slowly over a period of time, and eats while or before drinking, he is unlikely to become even mildly intoxicated, because under these conditions the alcohol can be disposed of as fast as it is absorbed.'

'The severity of the effects of alcohol depends largely on how much one drinks. In a quantity short of a lethal dose, alcohol has no adverse organic or structural effect on any organ, tissue, or cell. But because of its depressant action on the central nervous system, it may in proportion to the quantity present in the blood, interfere with the functions of many parts of the body. This functional impairment is reversible; that is, the activity of an organ returns to normal after alcohol leaves the body, providing there are no accompanying complications such as poor nutrition or infection.

Alcohol is not a direct cause of permanent damage, although in excessive quantities, or in the case of individuals who are unable to tolerate any amount of alcohol, it may trigger dormant or unrecognized disorders.

Even one drink might diminish the efficiency of the brain, and many can anaesthetize it as effectively as ether. The brain's highest functions, those centered in the cortex, are dulled first. Inhibitions may be lowered, judgment may become less keen, anxieties may seem to diminish, fatigue may be masked, and movements may become clumsy. The lowered level of performance may threaten safety and well-being when the time, place, or occasion of drinking requires optimum efficiency. Conversely, under circumstances appropriate for relaxation, small quantities of alcohol may be beneficial.'

'The exact nature of alcoholism and its specific causes are not yet known. Research indicates that there may be many kinds of alcoholism derived from many causes. Some of the causes may be metabolic, physiological, psychological, or sociological, but it is likely that each of these factors has a share in causing alcoholism.

Alcoholism is an illness which may be treated but not entirely cured. The treatment involves an individually tailored program which may include drugs, nutritional therapy, psychology, psychiatry, religious and spiritual counseling, social welfare, recreation, and family counseling. Many alcoholics have responded favorably to such programs.

Because of the limits of our knowledge, total prevention is not yet possible. But partial prevention can be expected through sound education programs, of which instruction in schools is a part.'

Since it is pretty obvious that in our society unwise drinking causes much distress and may even lead to alcoholism, yet any attempt at prohibition would be doomed to failure, what do we tell our young people? In the first place we tell them the facts – all the facts that they are capable of understanding, not just those we would like to select because they fit in with our preconceptions. Then we must try to get them to think about alcohol, its place in our society and the place it is going to occupy in their lives. Since most of them are going to drink at some stage of their lives, probably whilst they are still young and inexperienced, it is up to us to teach them how to drink wisely.

Care must be taken not to frighten them too much. Apart from the fact that fear is often counter-productive, many of them will have parents who are heavy drinkers and we need to be careful about making them too anxious about their parents. The fact that youth likes to live dangerously, to take deliberate risks, is another reason for not over-emphasizing the dangers. We should rather concentrate on how to drink wisely. Our present licensing laws, the legal age limit, and the fact that children are not usually allowed in public houses all tend to give an aura of glamour to the drinking of alcohol. If alcohol is for adults, then by drinking they vaunt their desire for adult status. Would it help if we removed the legal age of drinking? By doing so we would remove the barrier that provides such a challenge to those old enough to want to be old enough to drink. If children were allowed in public houses, the character of the pubs would change. They would become more social family centres instead of places whose serious business was the imbibing of alcohol. There is, of course, a certain amount of masculine resistance to this idea but I think the men will find that they have gained more than they have lost. In any case, the day of father getting away from it all and leaving mother to cope is over. He is now much more a part of the family and usually finds his new role rewarding.

All these things can be discussed by senior classes and many of them by any secondary school class. They need to be discussed because we cannot ignore the ill-effects of over-indulgence in alcohol. Anywhere in the United Kingdom it is a far more serious problem than the abuse of illegal drugs, but in some areas it is a far worse problem than in others. No one is quite sure why this is; it is probably a mixture of tradition, culture, and social mores. Pupils would enjoy studying the local drinking habits and getting statistics on the involvement of alcohol in physical and mental ill-health, driving offences, and crime. Whilst it is the local figures that will be more meaningful, here are a few national ones against which the local figures can be compared. Scotland is notorious for its high rates of alcohol consumption, so the figures for Scotland are given and compared with those for England and Wales.

'In 1970 over 3000 patients were treated for alcoholism or alcoholic psychosis in Scottish mental illness hospitals. The admission rate for men was more than four times that for women. In 1969 admissions for these diseases accounted for 27 per cent of all male admissions to mental hospitals compared with 5 per cent in England and Wales.'[3]

'In 1970 47 deaths were recorded as due to alcoholism and 28 as due to alcoholic cirrhosis of the liver. The Scottish death rate was about four times that for England and Wales in 1969.'[3]

'It is estimated that the suicide rate among alcoholics is about 80 times that of other males of the same age.'[4]

It is widely assumed that there is a close link between the drinking of alcohol and the committing of crime, but, with the exception of driving offences, it is difficult to find proof of this. In a parliamentary debate in October 1972 an Aberdeen M.P. said that 'the police estimated that drink was an element in between 50 and 75 per cent of crimes, in Scotland'.[5] Even if we halved these figures before applying them to England and Wales, they would still be terrifying. What estimate do your local police give of the percentage of crimes in which alcohol is involved?

[3] *Alcoholism Fact Sheet No. 1*, Scottish Health Education Unit.
[4] *Alcoholism Fact Sheet No. 1*, Scottish Health Education Unit.
[5] *The Guardian*, 26 October 1972.

'The distribution of alcoholics in respect of marital status seems to differ significantly from the population at large. Moss and Davies (1967) found male rates of 136 per 10 000 among the widowed and divorced, 68 per 10 000 among the single and 55 per 10 000 among the married.... An American study yielded rates of 1050 per 10 000 widowers, 680 per 10 000 divorced or separated men, 290 per 10 000 single men, 250 per 10 000 for married men (Bailey *et al.* 1965).'[6]

This seems to show that alcohol is being used as an alternative prop when the support of the wife is lost, especially by death.

There is much still to be learned about the effects of alcohol and the causes of alcoholism. It is an interesting and important subject but let us not forget that for millions of people alcohol is a pleasant and beneficial way of lubricating the wheels of the social round.

Further Reading

Todd, Frances. *Teaching About Alcohol.* (New York: McGraw Hill, 1964.)
Furnas, J. C. *The Late Demon Rum.* (London: W. H. Allen, 1965.)
Office of Health Economics. *Alcohol Abuse.* (1970.)

[6] *Alcohol Abuse,* Office of Health Economics, 1970.

8
Drugs–Prescribed and Unprescribed

Drugs are substances which cause a chemical alteration in the function or structure of living tissue, and their use is probably as old as man himself. I would suggest that it may be older. Animals are believed to eat particular plants in an attempt to cure themselves when they are ill. Certainly, from as far back as we can trace, man has used drugs. Wise women and witch doctors have gathered herbs and brewed or otherwise prepared them. Trusting fellow mortals have obediently swallowed the resulting concoctions and, usually, felt much better for it.

So our belief in and our dependence on drugs is not new. What is new is the strength and variety of them at our disposal today. Doctors are flooded with literature about new, expensive, and powerful drugs. Even with all their training and conscientious desire to keep up with the latest developments it is impossible for any of them to assimilate completely all the information they receive. And yet some of these drugs could help to cure or relieve the suffering of their patients. They read as much as they can and, guided by articles in medical journals, they try out some of the drugs. Of course, all these drugs have undergone various testing procedures before they reach the doctor and many of them have been tested on animals, but the human body is a strange mechanism and does not always react to drugs, or anything else, in the way that we expect. So there is today, as with the medicine man of old, a certain amount of trial and error. Drugs do a great amount of good, they save lives, they ease suffering. But they all carry risks and there will always be some people who will react unfavourably to them. The best that can be said of any drug is that it does more good than harm to most people most of the time.

Even though there is this element of Russian roulette in drug taking, yet we continue to take them in increasing numbers. Every time we visit the doctor we expect to come away with a prescription. It used to be a 'nice bottle' we expected, but now it is pills. They come in all colours, shapes, and sizes, and we swallow them all down with hope and with a lack of sceptical discernment that is a touching testimonal to our faith in doctors. We never think to ask what side effects the drug might have. More important, we never ask what our chances of recovery would be if we took no drugs. Any visit to the doctor which does not result in a prescription is likely to leave us feeling angry and humiliated. After all, if he has not given us anything then he must think there is nothing wrong with us. He might have given us a lot of time, compassion, and wise advice, but without our drugs to swallow we feel that we have been given nothing. Knowing this the doctor usually gives us the much coveted prescription and we either take it, or put it in a cupboard and forget it, and feel better.

There are four reasons why we might feel better. One, the drug might have been effective. Two, our bodies recover spontaneously. Most illnesses are self-limiting and, given time, the body will gain control over them. Three, what we really needed was sympathy and understanding. By giving us a prescription the doctor admitted that we were feeling ill and that he wanted to help us. Sometimes this alone is enough to start us on the road to recovery. This can happen even without our taking the prescribed drug; it can do us good even while it sits untouched in the medicine cupboard. The fourth reason is an extension of the third, but it necessitates the actual taking of the drug together with our belief in its effectiveness. This can happen even with a completely inert substance – a placebo.

The phenomenon of the effectiveness of placebo responses is fascinating and is well known to all doctors. In a class experiment with medical students,[1] the students were told that they were going to be given tablets and were led to expect either a stimulant or sedative effect. Each student was given either one or two pink or blue capsules which had to be swallowed in the presence of the investigator. The class was not told that the colour and number of capsules differed. The students had physiological tests before and one hour after the drug was taken and at the same time they were asked to complete a psychological self-rating for desirable and/or undesirable effects.

'For the whole class sedative responses were six times more frequent than stimulant effects. There was a tendency for undesirable sedative and desirable stimulant effects to occur more often. The most frequent individual responses were the three undesirable sedative actions – i.e. drowsiness, sluggishness, and tiredness. 54 per cent of the subjects reported feeling more drowsy. The commonest desirable effects were the sedative responses of feeling more relaxed and less jittery, which were reported by 38 per cent of the subjects. The most common stimulant effects were the desirable ones of feeling more talkative, more cheerful and less sluggish, reported by 9 per cent of the class. Only three subjects did not have any change in response. . . . The pulse rate decreased in 66 per cent of the subjects and increased in 15 per cent. Similarly, systolic arterial pressure decreased in 71 per cent and increased in 18 per cent.

More pronounced (but not more frequent) changes were noted by those taking two capsules compared to those who took only one. . . . There were two significant differences due to colour, both indicative of the blue capsules producing more sedative effects than pink capsules; 66 per cent of subjects on

[1] *The Lancet*, 10 July 1972.

blue capsules felt less alert compared with 26 per cent on pink ; 72 per cent on blue capsules felt more drowsy compared to 37 per cent on pink. There was also a tendency for those subjects on blue capsules to feel more sluggish.'

It is, I am sure, unnecessary to add that, pink or blue, the capsules were placebo only.

I have quoted this experiment at length to re-inforce the very important fact that we are greatly influenced by the effect we expect the drug to have on us. We can even be influenced by its colour. This is true of heroin, aspirin, and cannabis as well as of the drugs prescribed by the doctor. We are not as far removed from either faith healing or fear of the evil eye as we would like to suppose.

Why do we respond in this way to a visit to the doctor or to swallowing a placebo? I cannot pretend to give a scientific answer but it seems to me that we are looking for sympathy and comfort. When we fail to get them from our families and friends we go to the doctor for them. If we cannot have the support of warm and sympathetic relationships then we try to lean on drugs instead. There is no great harm in this, although there might be a lesson on the need for improved relationships, but there are dangers. Often these dangers are unforeseen in spite of the rigorous testing of new drugs. One such danger is addiction. A classic example of this is the amphetamine group of drugs. They were given to relieve depression or to aid slimming, but many of the middle-aged women for whom they were prescribed became addicted to them. Young people too found that they could get a 'high' from Mum's pills and so the 'pep pill' cult began. It was all started, in ignorance, by doctors genuinely trying to help their patients. A similar story could be told about barbiturates. In many areas now doctors are voluntarily refraining from prescribing either barbiturates or amphetamines.

There is no point in blaming the doctor. He too reacts to what is expected of him. As I said in Chapter 2, the responsibility is ours. Ours too is the responsibility for all the millions of drugs that we buy from the chemist. The advertisements tell us that they will effect miraculous cures and often we have a relative or friend who has taken a similar preparation with good results. Our faith in the drugs our doctors give us overflows into the drugs we buy and administer ourselves. Often we do not stop to think either what effect the drug will have or whether this effect is desirable. If we get diarrhoea we rush to get a medicine that will stop it. Yet should we want to stop it? Why have we got diarrhoea in the first place? It may be an infection, in which case stopping the flow will certainly not cure it. It may be something which we have eaten to which our body is taking exception. One of the body's defence mechanisms for getting rid of poisonous substances is diarrhoea, hurrying the toxic substance through the intestine and out of the body before it can be absorbed. Does it really make sense to keep the toxic substance in the body so that it can be absorbed? The same applies to cough linctus; do we want to stop a cough which is clearing poisonous substance from the lungs? Trying to get rid of troublesome symptoms without finding the cause is just asking for trouble.

The most common drug of all is the pain killer. We have come to believe that we should never have to suffer pain and at the first sign of it we rush for an analgesic. I am not saying that we should all be stoics, just that we should weigh up the pain against the possible unpleasant effects of the pain killer and make an informed decision. The most common pain killer is aspirin in one form or another. Yet aspirin can cause irritation, and even bleeding, of the stomach lining. Phenacetin used to be popular but has now been banned in this country because it was found to be harmful to the kidneys. Paracetamol, which is advocated by U.K. doctors as the safest pain killer, is banned in Sweden because it is a derivative of phenacetin. The truth is that there is a risk in taking any drug, but in the case of aspirin and paracetamol the risk is very slight if the use is only occasional. Anyone feeling the need to take any of these tablets regularly should seek medical advice.

Discussion should centre round the role of drugs in maintaining health. There is great scope for mathematicians in working out the frequency with which particular drugs are taken in the local community. An investigation into the drugs that individuals have taken and their effects, desirable and undesirable, might prove instructive, as the same drug might have produced quite different effects on different people.

Further Reading

Burstan, G. R. *Self-Poisoning.* (London: Lloyd-Luke, 1970.)
Laurie, Peter. *Drugs.* (London: Pelican, 1967.)
Modell, W. and Lansing, A. *Drugs.* (Time Life Science Library, 1968.)
Teaching About Drugs. Curriculum Guide K-12, American School Health Assoc.,
    1970.

9
Drugs–Proscribed

Before going into the effects of these drugs we must first get the problem into perspective. In dealing with addictive substances I started with food, which is probably the most widely distributed addiction, then went on to smoking and alcohol because these are the chief causes of preventable ill-health and death. Of every 100 deaths in Great Britain in 1969, 24.45 were due to ischaemic heart disease, 13.97 to cerebrovascular disease and 5.14 to lung cancer. We know that smoking causes lung cancer and that both smoking and obesity play important roles in the causation of diseases of the heart and blood vessels. If we turn from deaths to hospital admissions we find that in 1968 there were 27 alcoholics admitted to mental hospitals per 100 000 of the population (males only) whilst the equivalent figure for drug addiction was 6. The total number of registered narcotic addicts for 1970 for the whole of the United Kingdom was 1430. Even allowing for the fact that there may be unregistered and therefore unknown addicts, it is still a very small figure. If we double it, it is still only equal to the number of alcoholics to be found in any one city.

If drug addiction is such a small problem numerically then why are we all so worried about it? I think there are several reasons for this. First, most of the misused drugs are relatively new to our particular culture and we are suspicious of them. Second, our methods of communication have so improved that we are aware of, and therefore able either to imitate or disapprove of, drug-taking anywhere in the world. Third, many of these drugs are taken purely for pleasure or to escape the unpleasant realities of today's world and we have an innate puritanical distrust of the pleasure principle. Fourth, the strange power of these drugs makes a lot of people afraid of them and this fear is re-inforced by our lack of knowledge of their long-term effects. Fifth, there is our subconscious worry about our increasing dependence on drugs, both legal and illegal.

Now for the drugs themselves. They are normally divided into three categories (the stimulants, the depressants, and the hallucinogens) which I will use for the sake of convenience.

The Hallucinogens

Cannabis

This is the most widely known of all the illegal drugs and, so far as our present knowledge is concerned, it is also the least harmful. There are many names, about 250 in all, for cannabis, which is the product of the Indian hemp plant. There is marihuana, which comes from the leaves of the plant, and hashish, made from the resin of the plant, which is stronger. Slang names include pot, grass, shit, and tea. It is usually smoked mixed with tobacco (reefers), but can be eaten in cakes or sweets. When it is eaten its effects become evident much more slowly than when it is smoked. This delay in the onset of the effects can result in too much of the drug being taken. When it is smoked it gives off a peculiar 'sweet' smell which is easily recognized by those who are familiar with it. Its effects are similar to those of alcohol, although the body chemistry is different. It produces relaxation, mild euphoria, a lowering of inhibitions, and a distortion of time and space. Driving under the influence of cannabis is just as dangerous as driving under the influence of alcohol. There are, however, differences between the two drugs. One of the main ones is that whilst alcohol apparently releases aggression, cannabis induces quiet contemplation. Also the body becomes accustomed to the effects of alcohol and needs, as time progresses, larger doses to get the same effect; this is known as tolerance. With cannabis tolerance does not happen, in fact an experienced user can get the same effect by using smaller amounts more efficiently.

In the nineteenth century Queen Victoria set up the Indian Hemp Commission to investigate the effects of the drug. Since then, right up to the recent Wootton Report, there have been several investigations, none of which has been able to produce proof of damage done by cannabis. Yet there is still controversy. Many 'experts' believe that it is harmless and would be in favour of legalizing it, others agree that it is apparently harmless, but they point out that for a long time tobacco was considered harmless and is now known to be a killer, so they would not favour legalization until we know more about its effects. Yet another group of 'experts' believe that cannabis, particularly in large doses, can lead to mental ill-health. One investigation suggests that cannabis may lead to enlargement of the ventricles of the brain similar to that which normally takes place with age. This investigation was, however, carried out on a very small number of people who were all multi-drug users, so that the most that can be claimed is that cannabis *may* lead to an enlargement of the ventricles of the brain in certain circumstances and that further investigation is needed. Before leaving the subject of cannabis I would like to ask you to consider the following points.

1. If cannabis is legalized it will be in addition to, and not instead of, alcohol and tobacco.
2. Legal cannabis may be exploited by commercial interests unless safeguards are built into the legislation to prevent this.
3. Cannabis is usually smoked mixed with tobacco and although cannabis may be harmless, tobacco certainly is not.
4. If, as is often said, a lot of young people smoke cannabis because it is

illegal, then by making it legal we may encourage them to switch to something more dangerous such as L.S.D.

5. Opponents of cannabis claim that it is often the first step towards more dangerous drugs. If this is so it is largely because the illegality of cannabis makes cannabis smokers move in groups where illegal drugs are available. Of course cannabis and alcohol, by lowering the level of inhibition, make those who take them more susceptible to suggestion. Could it be that alcohol is so acceptable because it makes people aggressive and this fits in with our competitive society, whilst cannabis with its quiet contemplative effect is inclined to make people opt out of the rat race?

6. Now that the active constituent of cannabis has been manufactured synthetically as T.C.H., the case for legalizing cannabis (but not T.C.H.) has been greatly strengthened. T.C.H. is highly concentrated and dangerous to take, but by its very concentration it is easier and less dangerous to distribute so that pushers will get more money for less risk. If what we are concerned about is the health of our young people then perhaps we should consider making natural cannabis legal if only to deprive the sellers of T.C.H. of a ready made market.

L.S.D.

This is classed as an hallucinogen or psychotropic drug because it alters perception. The effects of L.S.D. vary tremendously from person to person. On a good trip all the senses are intensified and often mixed so that colour is heard and music seen. Small things become very significant. Some people claim deep mystical or religious experiences as a result of taking L.S.D. Others say that it increases their creativity although objective observers can find no evidence of this in artistic work carried out under the influence of L.S.D. One of the dangerous and disconcerting effects of the drug is the flashback. Days, weeks, or months after taking the drug the effects suddenly return without warning even though there has been no further dosage. If this happened whilst driving a car or working with machinery the result might be disastrous.

Whilst a good trip may give wonderful experiences, a bad trip can be horrific and may trigger off long-lasting psychoses. All the L.S.D. available in this country is manufactured illegally, often in small laboratories. There is no way of knowing the strength of any particular pill or dose and there is also the risk of adulteration. It is said that many bad trips are caused by the impurity and incalculable strength of the drug as it is at present available. The expectations and mood of the drug-taker together with the environment in which the drug is taken are also said to influence the type of 'trip' that will be experienced. Some studies suggest that L.S.D. may cause damage to chromosomes and so affect unborn children, but this has been denied. Certainly the L.S.D. that is available is uncertain stuff to experiment with. It is colourless, odourless, and tasteless. Whilst it is often taken as a pill, it can be a liquid and a few drops may be added to a drink or taken on a lump of sugar.

The stimulants

The most common stimulants are tea, coffee, and coca-cola on which most of us depend to some extent or other. All stimulants act by stimulating the central nervous system. The cup that cheers is not an illusion. The amphetamine group of drugs including durophet, benzedrine, dexadrine, methedrine, and ephedrine are powerful stimulants. I have already said that many middle-aged people, especially women, have become addicted to amphetamines as a result of having them prescribed by a doctor as treatment for depression or obesity. The amphetamine drugs are also taken by young people to make them feel good and to help them to stay awake at all-night parties. Students take them before examinations and athletes before competitions. By masking the warning symptoms of tiredness they can push the mind and body to extreme exhaustion and have in this way been known to cause death. Many young people begin to experiment with pep pills to help them to feel confident and alert at parties; unfortunately tolerance soon develops and increasingly large doses are needed to get the same result. As the effect of the drug wears off, depression and an urgent need to sleep result and many young people take more pills to try to counteract this. In large doses the amphetamines can lead to a psychosis (the horrors) and admission to a mental hospital.

The depressants

The most widely used and most dangerous of these are the barbiturates. There are far more middle-aged and elderly people dependent on barbiturates as sedatives and sleeping tablets than there are young people taking them for kicks. To the young they are known as sleepers or downers. They are usually swallowed in tablet form but can be dissolved in water and injected into a vein, thus greatly increasing the danger. Barbiturates are killers and they are very addictive, so much so that sudden withdrawal from them without medical supervision can be fatal. In this way they are even worse than heroin. They are particularly dangerous because the margin between a 'normal' and a 'lethal' dose is very narrow. As one of their effects is to confuse the mind it is easy to take an overdose, which may be fatal. A mixture of alcohol and barbiturates is especially risky as each enhances the effects of the other.

Some people mix barbiturates and amphetamines, which may be injected into a vein as 'speed'. This is so dangerous that even the underground press has waged a 'speed can kill' campaign against it.

Today many doctors are replacing barbiturates by non-barbituric tranquillizers which are thought to be milder and safer than barbiturates.

Narcotics such as opium, morphine, and heroin also come under the heading of depressants. Heroin is the most powerful pain-reliever we possess. We would all support its use for easing the pain of terminal cancer but are unhappy when young people take it to ease their emotional pains. Heroin and the other narcotics give an initial euphoria which lasts for six to eight hours and then is followed by depression. Tolerance and physical dependence both develop fairly quickly. Larger doses have to be taken to produce the same effect, and if supplies are not available acute withdrawal symptoms including sickness, cramps, and cold sweats result. After a time even large doses fail to give the euphoric effects, but the addict has to have the drug in order to prevent withdrawal symptoms.

Glue sniffing

This is a dangerous practice which can cause great damage to the respiratory system. Since the glue is usually sniffed with the head inside a polythene bag there is also the risk of suffocation if unconsciousness occurs whilst the head is still in the bag.

There are many other substances used for 'kicks'. Even such innocent things as nutmeg, parsley, and thyme can be used for these purposes. What can we do about it? It would be ludicrous to try to outlaw them all. How many policemen would be needed to prevent us from growing parsley in our gardens? No, the law may make them more difficult, more dangerous and possibly more exciting to get, but it cannot banish them altogether. For every one that is removed from circulation another, possibly two, will be found to take its place. Perhaps the most the law can do is to try to remove the more dangerous ones and to hope that the replacements will be less harmful.

If the role of the law is so limited, what can we as teachers and parents do? Again the answer is very little. If we try to do too much we may well make things worse. When the head of a drugs squad was asked by a teacher, 'What should I do if I discover that some of my pupils have been taking illegal drugs?' his answer was 'Nothing for twenty-four hours, sleep on it first'. No-one could give better advice. Action taken in a panic or on a wave of indignation is likely to do nothing but harm. But after twenty-four hours, what should we do?

First we need to be sure that the pupils are really taking drugs and this is not easy unless they themselves tell us. At every conference on drugs teachers ask, 'How do I know that one of my pupils is taking drugs? What are the signs and symptoms?' The best answer I have ever heard is 'If you write a list of the signs and symptoms of normal adolescence, and I write a list of signs and symptoms of drug-taking, then the two would be almost identical'. It is because of this that the problem is so difficult. Restlessness, apathy, clumsiness, inattention, rebellion – all these will be in both lists. It is true that sometimes there is dilation of eye pupils with certain drugs, but this is a far from infallible guide. Then there is the Monday morning syndrome; children arrive late looking tired and haggard. This is certainly an indication of an ill (or too well) spent weekend, but we must be careful of jumping to conclusions. If the use of a drug is involved it is far more likely to be alcohol than anything else. Often the only way to be sure that a pupil is using illegal drugs is to win that pupil's confidence.

And now let us suppose we are really sure. What action should we take? This depends on several factors. The first is how the certainty was arrived at. If we were given the information in confidence, have we any right to take action that will involve breaking that confidence? There is no easy answer to this, but I feel convinced that we have no right to betray a confidence without the permission of the person concerned. If we wish to reserve the right to divulge information then we should make this clear from the start. Absolute trust and honesty is essential if we are to help. It is true that there are times when we receive, in confidence, information which we feel calls for more help than we alone can give. In that case we must try to convince the confider that further help or advice is needed and try to get consent for seeking it. Only in extreme cases should we break this trust.

The second factor is the type of drug being taken, the circumstances under which it was taken, and the frequency and dosage. An occasional whiff of cannabis or a pep pill at a party call for no more than a sympathetic ear and a bit of wise advice. All young people experiment. They are curious about everything and we encourage them in this. If we applaud their initiative in climbing mountains or dismantling cars to learn their secrets, we must be careful not to jump on their curiosity about the effects of drugs. Most of us tried tobacco and alcohol when we were young. The great majority of teenagers who try drugs are just experimenting. Once they know what it is like they will pass on to new experiences. Any interference might have a bad effect. In the eyes of rebellious teenagers, anything adults get worked up about is worth spending time on. So many of the phases through which our children pass seem alarming at the time, but once they are over we wonder what we made all the fuss about.

If, however, it has gone beyond experimentation and become a regular habit or if it is a dangerous drug such as one of the barbiturates, then it is up to us to persuade them to seek help or to seek it ourselves on their behalf if we can do so without breaking trust. To whom do we go for help? The first persons to be considered are the pupil's parents. They are often the last people the pupil will want to have brought into the case and even the teacher may not expect them to be very helpful. But they have a right to know. If the case should end up in court, they will be justifiably indignant if the teacher has withheld knowledge from them. Then there is the family doctor. He is usually very helpful and has a whole army of specialists at his command. If, for any reason, it is not possible to contact the family doctor, the school health service doctor may be willing to advise. The police are usually both helpful and humane, but we must not forget that their first duty is to uphold the law. Probation officers and social workers can be invaluable, especially if the pupil is already one of their clients. The school health visitor is a useful link between the school, the home, and other agencies. She should know, or be able to find out, about the pupil's medical and social history and home background. Also she is a general practitioner of the health and social services with a knowledge of the specialist agencies available and where and when they can be contacted.

Whatever action is taken let us never forget that it should be for the *good* of the pupil concerned and of the other pupils in the school. In real life it is often difficult to distinguish between a drug-pusher and a drug user. Often drugs are passed on to friends with no profit motive, just as adults pass round cigarettes. Of course profit does enter into it sometimes. Anyone who becomes hooked on a drug is at the mercy of the seller and has to raise the money to buy the drug he needs. One of the easiest ways to do this is to sell some of the drug he buys to someone else at a profit. It is a sound capitalistic, if immoral, principle. In cases like this the cry for expulsion goes up. The expellers convince themselves that they are acting to protect the other pupils, and in a boarding-school situation they may be able to make out a reasonable case for sacrificing one or two pupils in the interests of the rest. In a day school, however, particularly a State school, this cannot apply. I say particularly a State school for two reasons. The first is that if the pupil is under eixteen years then he (or she) will have to be sent to another school so that the danger is not being averted, merely transferred. The second reason is that pupils at State schools are usually drawn from a particular geographical area. It is possible to remove the pupil from the school but not from the area. From 4 p.m. to 9 a.m. and all the weekend he will be free to mix with former schoolmates. Since expulsion will have made him a hero in the eyes of many, it will have increased, not decreased his influence. The effect of expulsion on the individual concerned must not be forgotten either. It pushes him out of the school community further into the sub-culture that has already got him into trouble. So far as I can see it helps no one, with the possible exception of the staff of the expelling school.

Fortunately the dramatic cries for expulsion and other drastic remedies are heard less now than they were. We are beginning to realize that drug taking is not some new and specially heinous sin, but an extension of our own habits of imbibing nicotine, aspirin, alcohol, and such like substances. Very few of us are in a position to cast the first stone and this fact is becoming more commonly recognized. Above all we need to try to avoid moralizing and righteous indignation. The more we highlight the subject the more serious it will become. People have always resorted to drugs for the relief of pain, as a means of escape, and for pleasure. Even animals may do it, certainly I have a friend who insists that her cat gets 'high' on catmint. The cat rolls about on the plant with an almost frantic abandon, then staggers about in a 'drunken' way with a blissful grin on its face. As the wife of an ex-dairy farmer I can vouch for the fact that cows have an insatiable appetite for apples, even fermenting ones. After an apply orgy they would sometimes stagger about in a suspiciously tipsy fashion. Robert Frost wrote about this in his poem:

'The Cow in Apple Time
... Her face is flushed with pomace and she drools
A cider syrup. Having tasted fruit,
She scorns a pasture withering to the root.
She runs from tree to tree where lie and sweeten
The windfalls spiked with stubble and worm-eaten.
She bellows on a knoll against the sky.
... Her udder shrivels and the milk goes dry.'

That is all very well, but if our young people are to make an informed choice they need information and insight. How are they to get it? How to include drug education in the school curriculum without highlighting the subject is a very difficult thing. Once again it is much easier to say what we should not do, so let us start there. We should not engage in 'blitz' programmes as a result of some local or national scare. These do nothing but give publicity to the subject and focus interest on it. The same is true of isolated visits by outside specialists or solemn sermons by head teachers. We need to incorporate drug education into a comprehensive programme and we must make it seem a natural part of that programme. This can be done by using the idea of a support system, with 'drugs' as just one of the supports we use. Alternatively we can discuss the role of drugs in and out of medical practice, for by linking the two together we help to get the problem of proscribed drugs into proportion. Similarly it is a short and unemotional step from the effect of food on the body to the effect of drugs. There is no one 'right' way; everyone must deal with it as he thinks best.

The only hard rule that we can lay down is honesty. We need to tell them the truth as far as we know it and we must not be afraid to admit that there is much that we do not know. Many teachers are afraid of this subject because they feel that their pupils may know more about it than they do. This is not often the case, but where it does happen it can be put to good use. If pupils make statements that the teacher doubts but lacks the knowledge to disprove, then research into the truth of the statement will make useful homework for the pupils as well as the teacher. Whilst we want to make sure that young people have as much factual knowledge as possible, it is useless for us to try to convey this knowledge formally. They have to accept it emotionally as well as mentally and they are more likely to do this if they have helped to discover it, which is another argument for the research method of working.

I said that we should avoid moralizing but that does not mean that we should avoid discussion of the moral implications of drug taking. It merely means that we should allow them to think through to their own conclusions rather than try to impose our ideas on them. But let us be careful not to inflict too much on them too soon. Drug education should start in the primary school with the value of drugs in our society. By examining the effect of drugs such as penicillin and aspirin we can instil a respect for the powerful way drugs act upon the body. This gives us a solid base on which to build in the secondary school, but we should build on it slowly and carefully. Tobacco is the first of the addictive drugs the children are likely to try, and this is followed closely by alcohol. These are the drugs with which we should start and from which we can gradually move on as the pupils mature. The speed at which we go will be largely determined by the area in which the school is situated and the age at which they are likely to be exposed to any particular drug.

One final word of warning to young progressive teachers. I have said that cannabis appears to be less harmful to health than tobacco or alcohol and I would tell my pupils this. But, and it is a big but, the imbibing of cannabis is illegal and the penalties for breaking the law are heavy. These penalties are, in our present society, part of the side effects of cannabis. They are serious side effects and need to be stressed. It may be a reasonable thing to work for the legalisation of cannabis, but not to encourage young people to break the law.

Further Reading

Cannabis. The Wootton Report. (London: H.M.S.O., 1968.)
Laurie, Peter. *Drugs*. (London: Pelican, 1967.)
Misuse of Drugs in Scotland. Scottish Home and Health Department, 1972.
Schofield, Michael. *The Strange Case of Pot*. (London: Pelican, 1971.)
The Little Red School Book. Stage I, 1971.
Young, Jock. *The Drugtakers*. (London: McGibbon and Kee, 1971.)

imbibe – to absorb, to receive into the mind

10
The Physical Changes of Adolescence

Puberty is the age at which a member of either sex becomes capable of parenthood. So says the dictionary, making it all sound very simple. But as any parent will tell you it is far from simple and gives rise to unforeseen difficulties. Why does something so inevitable and universal cause so much trouble?

What actually happens and at what age? Somewhere between nine and fifteen years in girls and between eleven and sixteen in boys the pituitary gland starts sending out developmental hormones which signal the onset of puberty. First there is the growth spurt. The long bones increase in size, making carefully stocked wardrobes useless almost overnight. (Our daughter grew two inches in two months.) At the same time the body begins to take on the shape characteristic of its sex. Girls begin to get rounded hips and tummies, their breasts develop and hair begins to grow in their armpits and over their pubic areas. Boys retain their slender hips but develop wider shoulders and their genital organs increase in size; they too grow hair in the pubic region and under their arms, but in addition they begin to produce hair on their chests and faces. All these secondary sex characteristics are just the outward and visible signs of inward developments.

Inside the girl's body the ovaries are getting ready to produce ripe ova and the uterus is getting ready to receive them. Towards the end of puberty an ovum is produced, and passes along one of the fallopian tubes to the uterus, which has developed a thick lining in readiness for nourishing a fertilized egg. As this egg is not fertilized, and the first few eggs are not thought to be capable of fertilization, the lining is not required. It is shed and passes away as the menstrual flow. Since the early uterine linings are neither rich nor thick, the first menstrual flow is likely to be very scanty. Also at first the ovaries have not settled down into a rhythm, so that egg production and consequently menstrual flow are likely to be very irregular. Many girls have a gap of six months between the first and second period, others have regular monthly periods from the start. Both these are normal and so is any rhythm, or lack of it, between the two. Eventually nearly all women settle down to a cycle which gives them a period every 20 to 33 days. The classic period comes every 28 days but anything from 20 to 33 days can be considered normal. Even a settled rhythm is a very sensitive thing which can be disturbed by an illness, a change in the way of life (e.g. from a sedentary to an active job or *vice versa*) or an emotional upset. This is still more true of the unsettled rhythm of a young girl. A wider realization of this would prevent much of the worry that often accompanies any variation in the menstrual cycle.

Many of the books that I have read, usually written by men, have exhorted girls to welcome the onset of menstruation as a sign of dawning womanhood. I am sure that there are a lot of late-developing girls who have welcomed their first menstruation as a sign that they were not going to be different from their friends, but this is very different from welcoming menstruation as a blessing in itself. It is traditionally known as 'the curse' and for many women it has certainly earned that name. For the more fortunate ones it is no more than a nuisance, whilst others dread it as a time of agony. How then do we prepare girls for it? We must be honest and that means avoiding the sentimental male opinion 'women are here to bear pain'. Few of us are masochist and we need to fight this idea of pain as our birthright; it is one of the most damaging attributes of our patriarchal society. Similarly we must avoid telling girls that menstruation is something to be dreaded. In this, as with drugs, the effects we get are influenced by what we expect. If we tell girls to expect pain they are far more likely to experience it. Can we not be straightforward and honest? Menstruation is a normal function; it happens to every woman for more than half her life. Most women find it a bit of a nuisance but manage to cope with it without letting it interfere with the normal activities of life. There are a few who get discomfort or even pain but this should not be accepted as women's inevitable lot to be endured (or enjoyed?). Any girl who suffers from dysmenorrhoea should seek treatment and I do not mean the mere taking of analgesics. There is nothing wrong with taking drugs to avoid pain as a temporary measure, but we need to seek the cause of the pain and try to remove it. Girls with severe problems need medical help, but many can help themselves. Here, as in other spheres, the advice given in Chapter 3 is valid; basic health is half the battle. There is a book called *Periods Without Pain,* by Erna Wright (see Further Reading), which uses similar methods to those that have been so effective in removing the pain from childbirth. We need more research into ways of easing the physical discomforts of women and it is up to us to see that we get it. It is no longer good enough to say that this is woman's lot and we must endure it. Women need to liberate themselves from the pain and tyranny of their own bodies.

Not that girls have all the troubles, boys have their share of worries as their bodies develop. Their genital organs increase in size, the testicles begin to produce the male hormone testosterone which produces the secondary sex characteristics, and the testicles also begin to produce sperm. At this stage the boy starts to have spontaneous erections and emissions often accompanied by erotic dreams. These wet dreams or nocturnal emissions can be a source of great anxiety if their purely physical origin is not understood. Boys get

patriarch, one who governs his family by paternal right.

worried by the erotic thoughts that often accompany them and by the tell-tale stains the emissions leave on underclothes or pyjamas. Not all boys are concerned about this but a casual reference to it, explaining the naturalness of it, could save some boys a great deal of unhappiness.

In both sexes at puberty the sebaceous glands in the skin become very active and are inclined to pour out too much oil, thus making the skin greasy. They frequently become blocked, giving rise to the blackheads and infected spots that constitute teenage acne. The treatment of acne consists of following the basic rules of health, particularly ensuring an adequate supply of vitamins and frequent and thorough washing. More frequent washing is also needed at this time because from puberty perspiration in both sexes starts to smell as soon as it gets stale. Before puberty children are able to get away with infrequent washing and still avoid the unpleasant smell of perspiration; now they need to be warned that this is no longer the case. During menstruation girls need to wash even more frequently. There is no reason why baths should be avoided or hair left unwashed at this time. In fact baths are more necessary and hair, which is often lank during a period, will certainly look better for a wash. There is, however, absolutely no need to use what are euphemistically called 'intimate deodorants'. No one can tell by smell when a woman with good personal hygiene is menstruating. The advertisers have played on our sexual insecurity and embarrassment and made us afraid that we may smell at these times. Having cleverly created that fear they have marketed a product to remove it. Not only are these deodorants a waste of money but they can be dangerous. Most of them contain hexachlorophane which can irritate the mucous membrane of the vagina. It has even been suspected of causing damage to an unborn child. It is perfectly all right for young unmarried girls to use tampons if they can do so without too much discomfort. Young girls, particularly small ones, may find it difficult to insert them. With practice, however, most people can learn to put them in easily, and once the art is mastered they give a great deal of freedom. They give freedom from the fear of smelling, because the menstrual flow has no smell at all until it comes into contact with the air. They give freedom from the nagging worry that a bulky sanitary towel might be showing through a tight dress or trousers. Finally, and most important of all, they give freedom to take part in all activities, even swimming.

With this growth spurt, this sudden production of sperms or eggs, this taking on of a new shape, this great activity of all parts of the body, there is often a feeling of tiredness. How often do we hear older people, perhaps even ourselves, say 'you can't be tired, you are young'? But the young adolescent is often very tired. Mere physical development is using up so much energy apart from all the emotional and mental strain involved in growing up. A lot of the apparent laziness and apathy of youth can be just plain tiredness. This is not intended to suggest that we coddle our teenagers and sit them down with their feet up. Rather the contrary, they need exercise to get this new body into good shape. A lot of the time they are overflowing with energy and should be encouraged to use it, but we should not be surprised when they suddenly collapse with apparent exhaustion or spend a whole day mooning around doing nothing, or what looks like nothing to us.

Another by-product of this physical growth is clumsiness. This does not afflict everyone but we have all seen the adolescent whose arms and legs seem too long. We are used to our bodies being the size they are, we are skilled in manipulating them. For teenagers who grow suddenly bigger, it is not so easy; they put out an arm and knock something over because it stretched further than they expected. It can be very disconcerting, like suddenly being given a big car to drive after years of controlling a Mini. We only make things worse if we draw attention to this clumsiness. It is a phase that will pass and we should be patient and tactful.

I have not gone into details of the anatomy and physiology of the reproductive systems as these are usually covered in biology or a general science course. It is as well, however, to make sure that the pupils have covered this before discussing the above changes with them. For teachers working in schools that do not cover this I have included a list of very simple books that would give a sufficient understanding of the working of the reproductive organs without going into unnecessary detail.

Further Reading

Elgin, Kathleen. *The Female Reproductive System.* (London: Franklin Watts, 1969.)
Elgin, Kathleen. *The Male Reproductive System.* (London: Franklin Watts, 1969.)
Hughes, D. T. D. and Marshall, P. T. *Human Health, Biology and Hygiene.* (Cambridge University Press, 1970.)
Wright, Erna. *Periods Without Pain.* (New York: Tandem, 1966.)

11
The Emotional Changes of Adolescence

The physical changes of adolescence are accompanied by equally pronounced emotional changes. Puberty is a time of transition from childhood to adulthood. Just as the child has to learn to live with and to control a rapidly growing body, so he has to learn to control an equally rapidly growing personality. All his life adults have been people who had to be looked up to, physically as well as metaphorically; now he suddenly finds that he is as tall as, possibly even taller than, his parents. He no longer needs to look up to them physically and, aided by this equality of height, he begins to look at adults more critically. Many adults find this critical gaze very disconcerting.

As adults we are used to controlling our own lives. We decide what we will eat or wear, what time we go to bed and how we spend our money. We may feel that our freedom is very limited , but seen through the eyes of a child it is tremendous. No one ever appears to push us around in the way that children are being continually pushed about. Every child covets that freedom. This can be seen from an early age in children's games. They will order dolls, animals, and each other around in tones of voice that are replicas of their parents'. They would love to order us around but we are too big. And then, suddenly, we are no bigger than they are. If they are as big as us why can they not do as we do? So, we start to get insurrection and trials of strength, trials which the adults do not always win. Trials which the adults *should* not always win. All reasonable adults want young people to achieve eventual independence. Most of us are willing to help them to do it, but we can see the pitfalls and dangers, we have trodden this path and we want to lead them along it gently and safely. This usually means slowly. They are not interested in safety and they want to rush along at top speed. This worries even the most progressive adult. We tell ourselves that we are worried because they are not yet ready for the responsibility of freedom, they will make a mess of it and get hurt. Perhaps, although we do not admit it even to ourselves, we are loth to relinquish our power over them. Let us remember that similar arguments have been used by every colonial power that was reluctant to give freedom to those under its control. I think we might try to encourage our young people to go slowly, but we must avoid impeding them. Perhaps I should have said trying to impede them, because any victories we have in this battle will be short-lived if they are won by force.

What freedom are they looking for? At first they want very simple ones, to be able to dress as they like (or as the group dictates), to go out with whom they like, and to come in and go to bed at times of their own choosing – simple things, but very irritating to adults. How far should we give way? Compromise is usually the best, in fact the only answer. Take clothes as an example. I think that it is reasonable to insist that they avoid clothes, or hair-styles, that could constitute a danger to themselves or others, but only at such times as they are dangerous. It is all right for us to insist that long hair should be tied back or otherwise controlled in laboratories or workshops, but apart from this we have no right to interfere with their freedom to wear their hair in the way they want to. If we are genuinely worried about the transmission of head lice we may be morally right, although unwise, to try to insist on some standard of cleanliness, but we need to be sure that it really is lice we are worried about. So often our own deep prejudices parade in such disguises. Then there is school uniform. We complain about youth's insistence on conforming to the modes of the group, yet all too often we insist on uniform. I have no objection to a voluntary uniform and I too like to see rows of neat identically dressed children; it satisfies the neat and tidy part of my mind. But is it the best way of encouraging them to develop their own individual personalities? Individuality is something to be encouraged, not quelled. There is one point on clothes, however, where I would stand firm, a very appropriate phrase as I mean shoes. Shoes are the most important item of clothing, as teenage feet are still growing and can very easily be damaged for life. I would recommend freedom to follow fashion, however hideous we may think it, in everything but shoes. In shoes I would let them have the most garish colours, but would insist on correct design and fitting. I think the same principle of 'give way whenever you can and stand firm when you must' can be applied to everything.

In schools we should make far more use than we do of their need for independence and freedom. We are supposed to be training them to be responsible and to take their place in a democracy. How much responsibility are we willing to give them? If we wait until they can use it properly, how are they ever going to learn? We acquire all our skills through practice. Again, how many schools are really democratic?

At what age does a child become an adult? For voting, getting married[1] or taking out a hire purchase agreement it used to be 21 years, now it is 18 years. For obtaining a driving licence it is 17 years and for being able to buy a drink with a meal or leave school to earn a living and try to achieve financial independence it is 16 years. Are these different ages part of a carefully worked-out scheme of allowing our young people a graduated entry into adulthood, or are they just part of an accidental and rather muddled

[1] With parental permission, marriage at 16 is legal.

situation? This would make a fascinating project for a senior class. Most primitive peoples have some form of initiation ceremony which marks so clearly the moment at which a child becomes an adult that there is no point in anyone who has not undergone this ceremony pretending to be part of the adult world, for everyone would recognize it as pretence and treat it as a childish game. We have no such ceremony; if we had it might save us from some of the troubles caused by young people trying to convince the world that they have achieved this much coveted adult status. They do it by under-age smoking, drinking, and driving, by dressing older than their years, by challenging the authority of home, school, and law, and generally making a nuisance of themselves. Who can blame them? We have created a society where the ones accepted as adults are those who can put on the best show of having joined the club. Perhaps we need a really dramatic initiation ceremony with some visible insignia that could not easily be copied by the uninitiated. Maybe young people themselves could think of something as permanent as, but less painful than, a facial tattoo or a ring through the nose. If this initiation carried the real privileges such as being able to vote, drive a car, and earn a living, and if we made them pass it by means of some proof that they were useful citizens, then it might be just the incentive needed to channel youthful energies into constructive channels. It must not, however, become an academic award with still further privileges for the intelligent. The qualities needed should be concern for other people and for the environment in which we live. It is an idea that could easily be misused as a weapon for depriving certain people of full adult citizenship. To be sure that this does not happen we shall have to set standards that are attainable by everyone but which are still meaningful. This will be difficult but it should not be beyond the wit of man. People have been talking about our need for an initiation-into-adulthood ceremony for a great many years. It is time someone worked one out. Maybe your class could make a start.

A complication of this uncertainty about their place in society is the adolescents' uncertainty about their identity. So much is changing that they are bewildered. One minute they feel as much of a child as they have ever done and then suddenly they feel wise and mature, able to take charge of their own lives. These moods alternate with startling rapidity, making them difficult to live with. They even find themselves difficult. This is made worse by adults who expect them to 'be their age' and behave in a mature way but refuse to give them the privileges of maturity because they are not yet old enough for them. Both adults and adolescents want to have it both ways and this inevitably results in conflict. Not that all conflict is bad. They need to try out their new ideas, their new personalities. Arguments and friendly battles are excellent proving grounds for them. The difficulty is in trying to keep the arguments and battles friendly; it is so easy for bitterness to creep in, but if when the heat of the moment is past we can show them that the battle has not damaged our basic regard for them, then little harm is done.

This search for identity and independence is complicated by dawning, or should I say maturing, sexuality. Sexuality arrives on the scene in babyhood and is present in one form or another throughout childhood. At puberty it assumes a new, sometimes almost overwhelming significance. There are three types of sexuality, auto, homo, and hetero, and the adolescent is likely to try all three. There is nothing new about autosexuality. Babies handle their genitals and obviously derive pleasure from it. Masturbation is frequently resorted to by young children in need of comfort. What is new at adolescence is the intensity of the emotion involved and the fact that it frequently ends in orgasm. The myths about masturbation are manifold. It used to be seen as a symptom of original sin and people went to great lengths to crush this wickedness. Most parents believed it to be physically harmful. Children were given awful warnings about blindness and insanity, as well as numerous more immediate punishments if they did not give up the terrible practice. Moralizing dies hard and we still suffer from the aftermath of these beliefs. Masturbation has been one of the last words to become accepted in respectable society and many parents are still shocked if they discover their children doing it. About 98 per cent of men and 68 per cent of women are known to masturbate. We only need to look at these figures to realize that masturbation is the norm and that it obviously does no harm. In fact by releasing built up sexual tensions it can provide a much needed outlet. Since we deny our young the opportunity for much in the way of homo- or heterosexual experience, then we should be thankful that they can get at least some satisfaction from autosexuality. There is, of course, always the danger of the pendulum swinging too far. I read recently in a 'women's lib' article that all women *ought* to have an orgasm three times a day by hetero- homo- or autosexual means. My immediate reaction was to ask, 'Before or after meals?' To make sex of any kind an *ought* is to destroy it. I hate to think of any child or adult feeling worried or guilty because they masturbate, but it would be equally bad to have them saying 'Oh dear, I haven't masturbated this week, there must be something wrong with me'. Let us just treat it as natural, a way of coping with sexual desire when other means are not available, something to be indulged in, or refrained from, as we wish. I have dealt with autosexuality at length here because I feel that it plays a very important role in the emotional development of the adolescent. So, of course, do homo- and heterosexuality, but I shall deal with them in subsequent chapters. There is no need to spend much time on masturbation during sex education in schools, all it needs is a reassurance that it is a perfectly normal harmless habit indulged in by most of us at some time in our lives.

The stage of an individual's development, relative to his or her peer group, is another common source of anxiety at this age. The early developers are self-conscious about their visible secondary sex characteristics and may well be teased about them by their peers. This teasing is, however, usually spiced with envy and this makes it much easier to bear. It is the late developers who really suffer. They are subjected to taunts of backwardness, called babyish, and sometimes even made to feel abnormal. Their friends tell them that maybe they will never develop and they half believe them. Small genital organs in boys and small breasts in girls also give rise to feelings of inferiority. The male myth that large sex organs are synonymous with virility dies hard. We need to make it clear that neither sexual attractiveness nor performance depends on either the size of the organs or the age at which they develop. The boundaries of normality are very wide and by stressing this we can avert a lot of needless worry.

Further Reading

Claesson, Bert. *Boy Girl Man Woman.* (London: Caldar and Boyars, 1971.)
Fleck, H. *et al. Living with your Family.* (London: Prentice Hall, 1965.)
Hemming, J. and Maxwell, Z. *Sex and Love.* (London: Heinemann, 1972.)
Schofield, Michael. *The Sexual Behaviour of Young Adults.* (London: Allen and Unwin, 1973.)
Schofield, Michael. *The Sexual Behaviour of Young People.* (London: Pelican, 1965.)
Winter, G. D. and Nuss, G. M. *The Young Adult.* (Illinois: Scott Foresman, 1961.)

12
Sex Roles

Boys are tall and have broad shoulders and muscular strength. They do not cry or kiss or show emotion. They have logical, mathematical minds, and are good with engines and electricity. Girls are pretty and dainty. They cry, preferably quietly and delicately, show a touching dependence on males, and are demonstratively affectionate. They have quick but superficial minds and are good at writing verse (not poetry), sewing, and cooking. Yes, of course this is a parody of the sex patterns to which we try to make our children conform but there is enough truth in it to make most of us feel uncomfortable.

Conformity to the expected sex role is usually sought by identification with the parent of the same sex. In primitive societies, and even in this country in the past, this was achieved by the child spending a lot of time with, and usually working with, the parent of its own sex. When the sex roles are clear and easily differentiated the child is able to know just what is expected of him.

In our society there is confusion because the roles of male and female are not so clear-cut, particularly in the middle classes. Parents may both go out to work and do similar jobs whilst father will help in the house with cleaning, cooking, and care of children. This gives our children a less clear sex role and militates against straightforward identification with one parent. Many researchers, including McCandless, have demonstrated that there is a more definite role played by men and women in the working classes so that the child has a clearer, if less warm and understanding, pattern with which to identify.[1] With the present trend towards a predominately middle-class society and the adoption by the working classes of many middle-class values, more and more children are likely to find the pattern for their sex role increasingly confused. McCandless also shows that a certain degree of cross-identification with the parent of the opposite sex is desirable for full human development. Is it too heretical to ask whether the working out of a sex role will seem as important in fifty or a hundred years time as it does now? A consideration of the views of Freud, Adler, and Jung would seem to be appropriate. First of all Freud:

'The anatomical distinction between the sexes must leave its mark on mental life. After the sight of the genital organs of the other sex, the girl feels

[1] McCandless, Boyd R. *Children, Behaviour and Development*. (Second edition.) Holt, Rheinhart and Wilson, 1967.

herself at a great disadvantage, falls victim to penis envy, and this leaves in-
eradicable traces on her development and character formation. As a result
of the discovery of the absence of the penis, women are as much
depreciated in the eyes of the girl as in the eyes of the boy and later perhaps
of the man. The feminine situation is only established, that is to say, the
woman only becomes secure, when the wish for the penis is replaced by the
wish for the child.'[2]

At about the same time Alfred Adler wrote the following passage:

'The less capability of woman is a palpable fable. A girl is daily subjected
to the argument that girls are less capable than boys and are suitable only
for unessential activities. A girl comes into the world with a prejudice soun-
ding in her ears, which is designed only to rob her of her belief in her own
value, to shatter her self-confidence, and destroy her hope of ever doing
anything worthwhile. One of the bitterest consequences of the prejudice
concerning the inferiority of women is the sharpest division and pigeon-
holing of concepts according to a scheme. Thus, masculine signifies
worthwhile, powerful, victorious, capable, whereas feminine becomes identical with obedient, servile, subordinate. Character traits which would seem
to prove this fallacious contention of the inferiority of women prove
themselves at a closer observation nothing more than the manifestation of
an inhibited psychic development. We do not maintain that we can make
what is called a talented individual out of every child, but we can always
make an untalented adult out of him. That such a fate overtakes girls more
frequently than boys in our day and age is easily understood.'[3]

Jung writes:

'How is man to write about woman, his exact opposite, for woman
stands just where man's shadow falls so that he is only too liable to confuse
her with his own shadow. The elementary fact that a man always pre-
supposes another's psychology as being identical with his own, aggravates
the difficulty and hinders a correct understanding of the feminine psyche.
Women's psychology is founded on the principle of Eros, the binder and
deliverer, while age old wisdom has ascribed Logos to man as his ruling
principle. . . .

We deceive ourselves greatly if we suppose that many married women
are neurotic only because they are unsatisfied sexually or because they
have not found the right man or because they still have a fixation on their
infantile sexuality. The real ground of the neurosis is, in many cases, the inability to recognize the work that is waiting for them of helping to build up a

[2] Quoted by E. M. Westervelt in Winter, G. D. and Nuss, J. M. *The Young Adult,*
Scott Foresman, 1969, p. 319.
[3] Ibid.

new civilization. We are all far too much at the standpoint of the nothing-but psychology. We persist in thinking we can squeeze the new future, which is pressing in at the door, into the framework of the old and the known.'[4]

Whilst accepting the basic soundness of Freud's theory of psychosexual development and admitting the remote possibility of some degree of penis envy in young girls (after all, in our society penis = privilege), it may be submitted that only a man could have made such a sweeping generalization based on such a small observation. Erikson, writing in 1964, said:

'The existence of a productive inner bodily space has a reality superior to that of the missing organ.'[5]

This is an attempt to correct the balance but we must be careful not to swing from penis envy to womb envy. Surely it all depends on how a small girl's first observations are handled. A simple explanation could be enough to satisfy the child and prevent any feeling of loss or inferiority. Adler's view that the psychological differences between men and women are due mainly to conditioning contains a great deal of truth. He implies that given equal expectation as well as equal opportunity there would be little psychological difference between the sexes. It is even possible that there would be little difference in muscular development and strength. The third statement by Jung is in accord with modern masculine ideas that women should not try to compete with men but that they have a peculiarly feminine contribution to make to the world.

We are not in a position to say which of the three is right. Until the difficulties set forth by Adler have been overcome and both sexes have equality of opportunity and expectation we shall not be in a position to judge how much basic psychological and physiological difference there is between the two sexes. Let us not imagine that we are anywhere near to this state of affairs. From the moment of birth girls and boys are treated differently and we expect them to behave differently. This brings us back to expectation again; our doctors behave as we expect them to, the effect of a drug on our body is greatly influenced by our expectations, children's intelligence quotients are thought to be influenced by the response that their teachers expect of them. Is it any wonder that the same rule applies here? In fact it applies more here than in any other sphere, because it starts earlier (at birth), lasts longer (until death) and is more widespread (it is universal). It is also very insidious; we all find ourselves doing it even when we have every intention of avoiding it. This has gone on for so long and fits so neatly into the pattern of our patriarchal society

[4] Op. cit. Winter, G. D. and Nuss, J. M. *The Young Adult,* Scott Foresman, 1961.
[5] Ibid.

insidious, underhand, deceptive

that man even tries to claim a biological basis for this sexual personality – typecasting. Here is an excerpt from Kate Millett's *Sexual Politics:*[6]

'In cases of genital malformation, and consequent erroneous gender assignment at birth, studied at the California Gender Identity Centre, the discovery was made that it is easier to change the sex of an adolescent male, whose biological identity turns out to be contrary to his gender assignment and conditioning – through surgery – than to undo the educational consequences of years, which have succeeded in making the subject temperamentally feminine in gesture, sense of self, personality and interests. Studies done in California under Stoller's direction offer proof that gender identity (I am a girl, I am a boy) is the primary identity any human being holds – the first as well as the most permanent and far reaching. Stoller later makes emphatic the distinction that sex is biological, gender psychological and therefore cultural: "Gender is a term that has psychological or cultural rather than biological connotations. If the proper terms for sex are 'male' and 'female' the corresponding terms for gender are 'masculine' and 'feminine'; these latter might be quite independent of (biological) sex."[7] Indeed so arbitrary is gender, that it may even be contrary to physiology: ". . . although the external genitalia (penis, testes, scrotum) contribute to the sense of maleness, no one of them is essential for it, not even all of them together. In the absence of complete evidence, I agree in general with Money and the Hampsons who show in their large series of intersexed patients that gender role is determined by post natal forces, regardless of the anatomy and physiology of the external genitalia. . . ."

Because of our social circumstances, male and female are really two cultures and their life experiences are utterly different – and this is crucial. Implicit in all the gender identity development which takes place through childhood is the sum total of the parents', the peers', and the culture's notions of what is appropriate to each gender by way of temperament, character, interests, status, worth, gesture, and expression. Every moment of the child's life is a clue to how he or she must think and behave to attain or satisfy the demands which gender places upon one. In adolescence, the merciless task of conformity grows to crisis proportions, generally cooling and setting in maturity.'

Because of these tremendous cultural pressures and expectations each personality is likely to develop little more than half its potential. We are all a mixture of masculine and feminine traits and if we encourage our children to develop them all, their individual lives and the life of the world will be enriched.

[6] Millett, Kate. *Sexual Politics.* Hart-Davies, MacGibbon Ltd., 1969.
[7] Stoller, Robert J. *Sex and Gender.* (Quoted by Kate Millett.)

There are biological differences between the sexes and there may be a biological basis for the predominance of certain characteristics in each sex, but until we rule out the influence of culture by allowing equality of expectation, we shall never know. Those who believe in this biological basis should have sufficient faith in their belief to allow it to be tested.

Teenage sex is greatly influenced by these expectations. Girls are expected to dress and to behave in a way which will attract the male, in much the same way that a flower attracts a bee or a butterfly. It may be a frivolous thought but I imagine most males would prefer the bee rather than the butterfly as a masculine symbol. They have been brought up to imagine that a sting in the tail is superior to beauty. But I think the butterfly may be a better way of describing the behaviour our culture still condones in its young males. They are allowed to visit, take what they can get, and flutter away to another flower. There is no cultural compulsion to turn what they have taken into sweet and nourishing honey.

This is only a fanciful way of describing the double standard. Whether we talk about butterflies flitting or wild oats being sown, the idea is the same. The young male is encouraged to use his sexual urges to have fun and to gain experience. In pursuit of this experience he is expected to use the typical masculine traits of dominance and aggression. His female counterpart is expected to dress and behave in such a way that she excites and incites the male to pursue her. She is then expected either to run so fast that she outstrips him or fight so hard that she defeats his efforts to 'master' her. How she is supposed to do this when she gets much less training in either running or wrestling than her male counterpart, remains something of a mystery.

Until recently the female was not thought to have much in the way of sexual desire, beyond, of course, a desire to please the male. This is really not very surprising when we consider the obstacles in the way of any female enjoyment of sex. The first and most overwhelming of these is obviously the fear of pregnancy. The second is ignorance of female anatomy and physiology; the clitoris and its role in sexual pleasure has only recently been openly acknowledged. The third is the cultural insistence on the passive sexual role of the female. The dominant male makes the overtures, overwhelms any 'natural' feminine reluctance, and as a reward gives her the blessing of his semen. She meanwhile is supposed to play a docile, passive role and receive the gift gratefully. Only the other day I was told by a male 'Of course the sex roles are different, the man gives, the woman receives'. But even in the language of the old double standard it is not so simple as that. Read any traditional romance and you will find that the man 'takes' the woman whilst she 'gives' herself, or rather her body, to him: a reversal of the dominant/passive, taking/giving relationship. Still the old sexual mores defy logic, so it is a waste of time trying to analyse them in such terms.

It is taken for granted that a boy will go as far as he can sexually and that it is the girl's job to say 'no further'. In the days when women were believed to have fewer and weaker sexual urges there was some foundation for this. But this belief has been made completely untenable by recent sexual research. Let me quote again from Kate Millett:

'The studies of Masters and Johnson prove that the female sexual cycle is capable of multiple orgasms in quick succession, each of which is analogous to the tumescence, ejaculation, and loss of erection in the male. With proper stimulation, a woman is capable of multiple orgasms in quick succession.

In view of the long-standing belief in the existence of a "vaginal orgasm" it might be emphasized that the clitoris is the organ specific to sexuality in the human female, the vagina being an organ of reproduction as well as of sexuality, and possessing no erogenous tissue save in the lower third of the vaginal tract, the nerve endings in these cells all deriving from and centering in the clitoris. While there is no "vaginal orgasm" *per se,* there is, of course, orgasm in vaginal coitus (and probably one of a different experential character than that produced by exclusively clitoral stimulation) just as on any occasion when the clitoris is properly stimulated. In heterosexual intercourse, female orgasm is due to the friction of the penis upon the clitoral head or glans and the labia minora of the clitoral area. . . . The clitoris, one might point out, is the only human organ which is specific to sexuality and to sexual pleasure: the penis has other functions both in elimination and in reproduction.

While the male's sexual potential is limited, the female's appears to be biologically nearly inexhaustible, and apart from psychological considerations, may continue until physical exhaustion interposes.'

So much for the now exploded myth of women's lack of sexual desire. We are living through a sexual revolution and our teenagers are bewildered by its conflicts. Having become familiar with their traditional sex role they find themselves caught up in the currents of a rapidly changing society. The popular press has given enough coverage to the findings of people like Kinsey, and Masters and Johnson, to make young people realize that our past attitudes to sex were false and hypocritical. They are struggling manfully to escape from them. But escape is not easy, for they are constantly being battered with the old idea of the double-standard by films, television, magazines, and, above all, advertisements. Then there is the question of what they can escape to and surely that is where we as teachers come in. If anything good is going to come out of the sexual revolution then we have to try to see that the baby is not thrown out with the bath water. More difficult is the task of trying to distinguish the baby from the bath water.

Let us not make the mistake of thinking that it is only women who need to be liberated from a repressive sex role. Men too are expected to fill their traditional role and it can be just as onerous as a woman's. They are expected to be dominant and aggressive, to 'get on in the world', never to show emotion or fear. It is a foolish inhuman expectation. Men have just as much warmth and feeling as women and need outlets for it. Many of them do not want to be aggressive or to dominate and a lot of them are weary of the rat race. What we need is not women's liberation but a human liberation movement. We all need to be liberated from the prisons of our sex roles in order that we can become full human beings. We all have a male and a female side to our characters; by allowing only one side to develop we never reach full potential.

Further Reading

Friedan, Betty. *The Feminine Mystique*. (London: Penguin, 1963.)
Hutt, Corinne. *Males and Females*. (London: Pelican, 1971.)
Mead, Margaret. *Male and Female*. (London: Pelican, 1950.)
Millett, Kate. *Sexual Politics*. (London: Abacus, 1969.)
Our Bodies Our Selves. Boston Women's Health Book Collective, 1971.

13
Teenage Sex

How do we help teenagers to cope with their sexual problems? In fact do they really need any help, is sex education in schools really necessary today?

For thousands of years men and women have managed their sex lives without any formal teaching. For millions of years nature has managed to get species to reproduce themselves without any conscious thought. The idea of sex teaching in schools is a relatively new one and we need to ask ourselves whether it has arisen to meet a new situation or if it is trying, rather belatedly, to meet a need that has always been present. Before we can answer that perhaps we should try to define what we mean by 'sex' and 'education for sex'.

If we are to take the narrow meaning of the mating of a man and a woman in order to produce a child, then little, if any, education is needed. Nature will achieve this without help from us. But if we envisage sex as a more lasting and meaningful relationship between two people, which may or may not result in the production of a child, but which should result in fulfilment and happiness, then young people need much more than their natural reproductive drives if they are to achieve it. It is, obviously, this second definition of sex with which we are concerned and which needs to be borne in mind when asking if the need for sex education is new.

In all monogamous societies, where a couple live together for a long period of time in order to provide a secure environment for children, it is desirable that the union should be a successful one. Even in cultures that do not emphasize personal happiness in the way that our culture does this is still essential, as all children benefit from a harmonious background to their development. To this extent help and guidance in personal relationships between the sexes has always been desirable and has often been provided by parents, priests, and friends. Today this sort of help is still available but is not considered to be enough, perhaps it never was enough, but it seems that our modern adolescents are faced with greater problems than were their ancestors and these problems need to be examined.

The first cause is greater freedom. Our ancestors often had their marriage partners chosen for them; more recently they chose for themselves but their choice was usually limited both by social class boundaries and by geographic ones. This meant that the married couple had at least their backgrounds in common. Today, there is a slight lowering of class barriers (although most people still marry within their own class) and this with the extension of travel gives young people virtually the whole world to choose from, a more exciting but more frightening task than that which faced their grandfathers. There is also greater social freedom. Young people are allowed out alone at a much earlier age, for longer periods of time and with less restrictions on the way in which they spend that time, than the young people of preceding generations.

Then there is the impact of commercial interests and the mass media. Our young people are being subjected to an unprecedented barrage of sexual images often used for the purpose of selling goods which may have nothing whatever to do with sex. A near naked female body may well be used to sell metal tubes; it draws the eye of the male, which is what the advertisers want. Every time a newspaper or magazine is opened or advertisements are watched on the cinema or television screen, the human body is seen being used as a selling agent. The advertisers know that everyone is interested in sex and they deliberately set out to stimulate that interest. This stimulation is added to by many films and television shows. More and more of the body is being shown, often in a way which is calculated to rouse physical desire in the watcher. Fashion too joins in with mini-skirts, bikinis, and hipster trousers, all designed to focus attention on particular parts of the body. The female on the advertisement page, the screen, or the stage becomes a model which many women feel they have to copy; this is reinforced by the romantic stories in women's magazines and by the fashion designers who flood the shops with imitations of the clothes the models wear. Much money is made out of these clothes and the frequency with which fashion changes. Women often say that they dress for other women, not for men, and to a certain extent this is true; all women are afraid of the critical tongues of the other members of their sex, but the fashion designers do not design women's clothes merely with the admiration of other women in mind. The designs are largely created with the idea of attracting the male. The same is true, in a less exaggerated form, of men's clothes. They are encouraged to have a 'he man' look to make them attractive to the female. All this can be disconcerting enough for the happily married adult but its effect on young inexperienced teenagers could be quite shattering. We see young girls dressed up in the height of fashion quite innocent of the provocative effect they may be having on their male companions. Similarly the young male finds his dawning sexuality stimulated at every turn and he may feel quite unable to control the emotions thus aroused in him. There seems to be no way of stemming the tide of sexual stimulation or of protecting our young from it; all that can be done is to help them to cope with it. If we can enable them to become less easily influenced by it, we may even succeed in reducing it. Because, if it ceases to be effective, the producers will soon abandon it.

There is too the effect of men's and women's magazines, strip cartoons, and romantic novels. The word romantic is used not in the sense of the 'romantic' poets or composers but in one of the Oxford dictionary definitions of the word – 'remote from experience'. The men's magazines are full of pictures of naked or scantily clad women and smutty jokes and stories; the sort of thing that a man would not want his wife nor anyone he respected to see him reading. They encourage men to think of sex as something to be made fun of and to be rather ashamed of; something to be discussed in the bar when there are no women present; something to be indulged in furtively. This leads to a double standard of behaviour, one for men and another for women; in fact two for women, for some women must be pure and above the sort of sex which the men joke about, whilst others are there to be used for the gratification of the desires of the male. Almost as dangerous are the women's magazines and poor romantic novels which are full of stories of love affairs based almost entirely on physical attraction and inevitably ending happily ever after with wedding bells. They are remote from the real lives of the readers and lead them to look for an ideal partner who will fit in with their romantic ideas of a lover, rather than with the reality of a flesh-and-blood person with whom they can live happily for the rest of their lives.

A lot of this rather furtive attitude to sex can be attributed to our puritan ancestors who felt that sex was at worst the work of the devil, and at best only a means of reproducing our kind. Man's id might enjoy it but his super-ego was always struggling to surmount his carnal desires. Women were never supposed to enjoy it at all (apparently they had no id) they merely suffered it in order to gratify their husband's lower nature (and so prevent him from going elsewhere for gratification) and, above all, in order to have children. This puritan repression of sex resulted in a subconscious obsession with it. As Ian Watts says:

'The cause of this duality . . . is presumably that the tabooed object is always an indication of the deepest interest of the society that forbids.'[1]

We have inherited the interest together with some of the prurient furtiveness. One of our earliest novels, Richardson's *Pamela*, is a good example of the way in which public prudery and the exaltation of chastity could be made into a fairly detailed study of a sexual relationship. It was:

'a work that could be praised from the pulpit and yet attacked as pornography, a work that gratified the reading public with the combined attractions of a sermon and a striptease.'[1]

Richardson has been, and is still being, emulated in this by novelists with far less literary talent. One of the critics of *Pamela*, the anonymous author of *Lover of Virtue*, was at a loss to understand why so many:

'"public-spirited pen-men" thought it necessary to employ all their art and eloquence to keep people in remembrance that they were composed of different sexes when "provident nature" unassisted could be trusted to "prevent the world from coming to an end"'.[1]

Ian Watts goes on to point out that novels like *Pamela* were made necessary

[1] *The Rise of the Novel*, by Ian Watts.

by the repression of the instincts of 'provident nature', combined with the increasing concealment of what our culture calls the 'facts of life'. He was writing about the repressive society of the eighteenth century, but it could still be relevant to the so-called permissive society of the present day. Where would the erotic drives of our growing children lead them if they were not repressed? To find the answer we must look at young animals and at humans in primitive societies. How do they prepare themselves for their sexual lives? The answer is by practice. For some considerable time before they are sufficiently mature for full sexual experience they practice, on each other, and, in the case of animals, on the mother as well, a form of love play. Left alone this is, no doubt, what our children would do, it is what the children of some cultures do with the full approval and active encouragement of the adults. But our children are not left alone, they are hedged in by prohibitions and conventions. The very thought of their adolescent children practising sex would fill most parents with deep alarm. Yet, in the case of every other art in which we wish to become proficient, there is need for practice. Why should there be one sphere where practice is not allowed? It is also the art where, once it is engaged in seriously, mistakes hurt most. Since our children are not allowed to be taught in nature's way by practising, then we have only two choices left. Either we leave them to muddle through as best they can or we try to help by at least teaching them the theory of the art. Theory may be a poor substitute for practical experience but it is all that we can offer at present.

There is still one other reason why we should give our children sex education in schools and it is, perhaps, the most important one of all; it is the long gap between full physical development and the opportunity of leading a fully satisfying sex life that is imposed on them by our present cultural pattern. Children are maturing earlier and it is not unusual for some girls to start menstruating while they are still at primary school. By the age of thirteen or fourteen years a lot of girls are physically capable of bearing children and the boys are only a year or two behind them. Yet such is the way in which our society is ordered that it may be ten years before they are able to marry and lead a full sexually satisfying life. Even if, in some cases, it is only about five years, that five or ten years is the time during which the young person's sexual drives are at their most insistent. The society which makes it so difficult for them to satisfy those drives at the same time bombards them with stimuli which intensify them. It is no wonder that we find many young people worried and anxious and in need of help. They also have a spurious air of knowledge which leads some adults to feel that young people know all that there is to know about the 'facts of life', so that there is no need for us to try to teach them about such matters. Nothing will dispel this illusion more quickly than Michael Schofield's book *The Sexual Behaviour of Young People*.[2]

[2] Schofield, Michael. *The Sexual Behaviour of Young People*. London: Pelican, 1965.

The book leaves us in no doubt about the sexual interests and activities of teenagers. As Michael Schofield puts it, 'between fifteen and seventeen the teenagers are learning fast'. They are beginning to practise sex at an age when such practice can easily end disastrously in an unwanted pregnancy or in emotional injuries so great that their future relationships with the opposite sex can be damaged for a long time to come. By the age of fifteen 85 per cent of girls and 75 per cent of boys have started dating and kissing, by sixteen it has risen to 95 per cent of girls and 85 per cent of boys. By the age of sixteen only 14 per cent of boys and 5 per cent of girls will have had full sexual intercourse, but between these two extremes there are progressive degrees of intimacy all of which may lead finally to sexual intercourse. This is usually not premeditated:

'The replies of the teenagers showed that very few of them had set out with the intention of having intercourse on that particular evening.

"It just seemed to follow on naturally." (Boy aged 17.)

"We were just sort of mucking about and it just sort of happened." (Boy aged 16.)

"We went for a drink, back to his flat. It just seemed to happen. I don't know why. I think he was the first boy I'd met that made me feel I really wanted to." (Girl aged 18.)

"You just get tired of kissing and that." (Boy aged 19.)

"I felt like it. I felt I was entitled to it after four months." (Boy aged 16.).[3]

Their reactions afterwards are very interesting:

'But this first experience was not always an unqualified success and did not always result in sexual gratification. Less than half the boys (48 per cent) and less than a third of the girls (30 per cent) said they liked it when they were asked for their reaction to this first experience of sexual intercourse. On the other hand some of them said they actively disliked it (7 per cent of boys and girls). More girls were ashamed (25 per cent) than afraid (15 per cent) and even some of the boys felt ashamed (10 per cent) or afraid (5 per cent).

The boys were more likely to express their feelings in terms of pleasure and enjoyment, or the lack of it. The girls were more inclined to describe their later reactions after the sexual excitement was over:

"I felt a bit older, that was about all. Everybody had been talking about it and now I'd done it. Something to tell my mates. You don't feel much of a person yourself afterwards; at least I didn't." (Boy aged 17.)

"Well I wouldn't say it was anything fantastic." (Boy aged 19.)

"Tears. Up until then I'd thought of it as something I'd wanted to save until marriage. It seemed so silly that I'd lost it all in one night." (Girl aged 16.)

"Hell, what's all the fuss about." (Girl aged 18.)[3]

[3] Ibid.

There is something very pathetic about these comments, they don't augur well for future sexual happiness. It is true that these are only a small percentage of teenagers, the ones for whom the strain got too great, the others being still under varying degrees of strain.

When we turn from the evidence of their interest and activity to that of their knowledge, the picture becomes more alarming. Most of the teenagers had heard of the venereal diseases but there was still some ignorance about them; false ideas and a belief in old wives' tales were widespread.

About half the young people would not be able to recognize the symptoms if they were infected. There has been much television publicity recently about the increased incidence of venereal disease but very little detailed description of the symptoms. Here are some of the teenagers' comments:

'"They say they've got to stick a red-hot needle right up you to cure it." (Boy aged 16.)
"It gives you spots on your face." (Boy aged 18.)
"Don't tell me anything about it. I don't want to know." (Girl aged 16.)
"I've never worried about it. I'm very careful myself." (Boy aged 19.)
"It can't be all that bad or they wouldn't put it on the telly."' (Girl aged 15.)[4]

It is no wonder that people do not readily go to clinics if the viewpoint of the first boy is widespread. The 'don't tell me' and 'I've never worried' answers are examples of ignorance and fear that could be very dangerous, but the last one is the most alarming. Is the television set taking on the role of comforter? If young people assume that nothing really 'bad' will be shown on television then it becomes a dangerous medium, especially with its present emphasis on sex and crime.

The most horrifying statistics in Michael Schofield's book, however, are those on birth control. Less than half the boys indulging in sexual intercourse always took contraceptive precautions and a quarter of them had never used any kind of birth control method. Of the girls only a fifth always took precautions whilst well over half said they never used any method of birth control. It was found that eight out of every ten girls having sexual intercourse were at risk. The survey found that girls had a very real fear of pregnancy but only 0·5 per cent of the girls had ever bought a contraceptive and nearly all experienced girls left it to the boy to decide what form of birth control he would use, if any. In view of the nature of the consequences which will almost always fall on the girl so much more heavily than on the boy, the girl's reliance on the male for contraception is alarming and almost incredible.

Finally in looking at the reasons why we should undertake sex education in schools we ought to ask if the teenagers themselves feel that they need and want it. Once again Schofield provides the figures, 70 per cent of the boys and

4 Ibid.

78 per cent of the girls disagreed with the statement – 'there is no need to teach about sex in schools, because you can find out all you need to know for yourself'. In a democracy these figures should be taken seriously. There can be no better answer to the question of why we should include sex education in our school curriculum than that the teenagers themselves feel a need for it. When it is added to the other reasons already set out it is conclusive.

This still leaves us with the question of the kind of sex education we should give, and the age at which it should be given. As with drug education it should be part of a continuing process starting in the primary school. It is, of course, only sex education in schools that should start at that age. True sex education starts soon after birth. As I have said in Chapter 12 the way we handle and treat our children determines their understanding of their sex role. In infancy too we lay the foundations of shame or openness. It is mentioned here because young people, the parents of the future, need to be aware of its importance.

But back to school: most primary schools are now giving their children lessons that include a simple explanation of the mechanics of reproduction and birth. These make a valuable foundation on which to build, but the secondary school teacher needs to know just what knowledge the pupils have been given and this calls for a degree of co-operation between a secondary school and its feeder primary schools that is frequently missing.

First year secondary school pupils[5] are usually experiencing the physical changes of adolescence. This is the time to see that they understand what is happening to their bodies and why. The second year[6] would be a good time for discussing the emotional changes. Many of them are worried by the sudden worsening of their family relationships. They often feel very guilty about this deterioration, and to learn that it is a normal and passing phase can bring such relief that the actual relationship may be eased. At this stage too they are becoming aware of sexual stirrings and an interest in their own and/or the opposite sex that they find disturbing. There is, however, at this stage a danger in talking more freely and frankly than the children are ready for. They are in rebellion against adults and do not believe that we understand them. This makes them enjoy keeping from us these new and exciting feelings which gain in intensity from being kept secret and which they feel we are incapable of appreciating. We need to tread gently here.

By the age of fourteen we should be considering the giving of information on contraception and venereal disease. The main increase in new cases of gonorrhoea occurs in girls between fifteen and nineteen years of age. At about fifteen years they are usually more willing to discuss these things openly and it is our job to help them to work out for themselves a new morality.

It is useless to say 'sex before marriage is wrong'. They will just ignore such an edict and anyway they are subject to such sexual stimulation that complete

[5] First year pupils in England – Primary 7 in Scotland.
[6] First year in Scotland.

abstention from sexual experience is impossible. There are, however, three paths this can take. The first, autosexuality, I have already discussed at length. The second is homosexuality. For children and adolescents this is just as natural and normal as autosexuality. Most of us have indulged in it at some stage in our lives. Sometimes it takes an overt physical mode of expression, although in the young it seldom goes beyond mutual masturbation. Usually, however, it stops short of the physical and finds its outlet in a close warm affection for a peer or a 'pash' on a teacher. For the great majority this is only a stepping stone on the road to heterosexuality. Why we so often regard it as something to be ashamed of is difficult to understand. Can it really be wrong to love and admire a body just because its sex is the same as your own? It is true that a minority who fail to make the transition to heterosexuality have a hard time because of the strong prejudices that still exist against homosexuality. For some reason women seem able to get away with it more easily than men. In Scotland overt homosexuality, even between consenting male adults, is still an offence against the law. I can see that we need to protect our young people against homo- as well as heterosexual assault, but why the law should interfere in the personal relationship of adults is far from clear. Homosexuality needs to be discussed in schools with sympathy and understanding, but not pity. Conformity is not something we should try to force on people, for when we do so we take terrible risks. How many homosexuals have made disastrous marriages in an attempt to conform to society's demands? Let us try to get our young people to be tolerant of these whose natural instincts lead them to a different way of life. They harm no one, nor do they add to the world's over-population problem.

There may be disapproval of homosexuality, but it is heterosexuality that causes most of our worries about adolescents. Following puberty they find the opposite sex beginning to take on a new and intriguing significance. They put new zest into teasing each other, perhaps start new forms of wrestling. Often they are disconcerted by these new feelings. Boys may well show their affection by pushing or shoving a girl or hitting her with their school bags. Girls respond largely by verbal taunts but they too can join in the pushing and shoving. Usually they are quite unaware of the reasons behind this behaviour until it develops into games like 'kiss-chase' when they discover that kissing can be something more than an excuse for chasing about, something more even than 'fun'. But even when physical contact has moved from pushing and shoving to hand-holding and kissing, it is still at first largely a group activity. It is at the next stage that they start to go off in pairs and this is where romance comes in. The natural idealism of youth, boosted and perhaps twisted by glossy magazines, films, and television, helps them to fall in love with love. They embark on innocent, passionate affairs with little regard for the personality of the object of their affections. What they want is someone to love. Usually at this stage it is love that predominates over sex and what sex there is is very romantic. These affairs are often short-lived but they may develop into something deeper and more real. As the adolescents develop, the objects of their affection become real people rather than symbols of devotion.

If at this stage, and I am thinking of fourteen to sixteen year-olds, love predominates over sex, why do adults worry? They do not look askance at idealistic love, in fact they find this rather touching and see it as a safe diversion from sex, which is the cause of their real fear. They worry because of the cases where sex predominates over love and it seems to me that worry is natural and inevitable, for they are only too well aware of the power that sexual desire can have in the young. They know that it can lead to unwanted pregnancy or venereal disease or a broken heart or an obsession that over-rides everything else. They want their young to be concentrating on passing examinations or getting good jobs, and sex gets in the way of these things. It is unfortunate that for most young people the time of their greatest interest in sex coincides with this period that adults would like to be devoted to the serious business of getting on in life. It is possible too that many parents would like to postpone their children's interest in sex because they see it as a threat to their own sexuality; it makes them feel old.

But whether we like it or not, we have to cope with the peak period of youthful sexuality when it occurs and not when we want it to occur. It would be simpler and more effective to alter the age at which they take examinations and seek jobs than to tell them to suppress their sexuality. During adolescence sex will not be repressed without disastrous results. We must accept that our choice is not between sex and no sex, it is between the three kinds of sex. As Dr James Hemming puts it:

'The choice for the adolescent years – we have to be absolutely clear about this – is not between sex and no sex but between natural sexual expression or some substitute for it. For the young male the substitute will, in over 90 per cent of cases, be fantasy-plus-masturbation. For the girl, the substitute is likely to be unbridled romanticism coupled with a lower incidence of masturbation.

To impose years of egocentric substitutes on adolescents is to obstruct the development of that sensitive reciprocity which lies at the heart of an enduring sexual satisfaction within marriage.

Those who make their choice against premarital love are making a choice for alternative outlets. . . .

It is an extraordinary fact that the only legitimate human capacity that is not welcomed, and encouraged to develop when it manifests itself, is sexual capacity. A child who shows a taste for reading is generously surrounded by books. A boy who displays ability in swimming or football is eagerly watched and fostered. Any sign of an interest in music is heralded with hope and opportunity. Only sex on its appearance is shunned and the attempt made to put it into cold storage for years on end – years when the vital complex of feeling, nerve networks and muscles, which provide the emotional, neural and physical basis for adult sexual capacity, need to be developed and refined, like anything else, through use and growth.

Values and control come through use not through denial. Starving people do not have good table manners. The beautiful grace and control of a dancer are not attained by not dancing. Discipline is a matter of the right use of our functions.'

The article from which this quotation is taken aroused a storm of protest, largely from Christians who seem to feel that if only they can postpone any physical expression of sexual desire until after marriage they have achieved something wonderful. Do they stop to think that they are probably forcing the young into what James Hemming calls fantasy-plus-masturbation? Perhaps they should reread the Sermon on the Mount: 'But I say unto you that whosoever looketh on a woman to lust after her hath committed adultery with her already in his heart.'[8] But perhaps it is accepted if it is only in the heart.

A more reasonable protest came from a woman teacher who was worried about the difference between boys' and girls' views on sexual experience. According to the essays she marked, the girls all had their sights set on marriage whilst the boys had other ideas. Some would argue that this is biological. The woman is looking for a secure base where she can rear her young. This might have been true once, but modern contraceptives have made it unnecessary and women are very conscious of this. The other reason for it is cultural and will take a long time to alter. Of course the girls' sights are set on marriage; they have been brought up to believe that this is the greatest thing that life has to offer them, and that any job they may take is only a stop gap until they become wives and mothers. Boys grow up with endless exciting ideas about the opportunities awaiting them. Marriage may fit into their plan, but being a husband and father is only a part of it. Until we give girls equality with boys in expectation of what life holds, we shall have these differences of outlook about the role of sex. Those who feel that sex plays too big a part in life could help by giving girls, and to a lesser extent boys, opportunities to fulfil themselves in other ways. If we did this we could safely leave sex to take its rightful place as one of the more important pleasures of life, not as the only means of fulfilment.

Further Reading

Bedoyere, Quentin and Irene de la. 'Choices in Sex'. *A Living Parish Pamphlet, 1973.*
Brown, F. and Kempton, R. T. *Sex Questions and Answers.* (London: McGraw Hill, 1970.)
Dollas, Dorothy. *Sex Education in School and Society.* N.F.E.R., 1972.
The Little Red School Book. (London: Stage I, 1971.)

---

[7] Hemming, Dr James. 'Sex and the Adolescent', *The Scotsman,* 25 June 1973.
[8] St. Matthew, chapter 5, verse 28.

14
Marriage or Not?

The English teacher who replied to James Hemming's article said that in their essays the girls all wanted to get married. Yet we are always reading in the press or hearing on radio or television that marriage, as an institution, is on the way out and that the family is breaking down. These two viewpoints would appear to be contradictory but I suspect that there is truth in them both.

First, the girls whose desire for marriage is reflected in their essays. Yes, of course they want to get married. They have been brought up to regard marriage as their main aim in life. Throughout their upbringing there has been the implicit assumption of the superiority of the male on which our society is built. By marriage they will prove to the world that they have sufficient sex appeal, or personality, to 'get a man'. It makes them feel wanted and useful and opportunities for getting these feelings in other ways are restricted if you are female. Then there is security; beyond the security of being loved and wanted there is the need of financial security. Men are much more likely to get secure and well-paid jobs. In addition there is the role of the woman, not only as child-bearer, but also as child-rearer. It is accepted in our culture, although it is now being challenged, that it is the woman who must sacrifice her career to stay at home to look after the children. This makes it necessary for her to find someone who will provide for her and for the children during this period. Since, until very recently, childless marriages were treated as incomplete, nearly every girl saw motherhood as an almost inevitable sequel to marriage.

Yet they say that marriage and the family are threatened and in a way I think they are. Women's liberation is opening up new horizons and girls are beginning to see that life may have other things to offer. Then there is the permissive society with its emphasis on freedom. Young people are becoming aware of what many of their parents may have felt but were afraid to admit, that marriage can be bondage. As another letter following James Hemming's article put it: 'Why is it that a relationship between a man and a woman only becomes socially acceptable when two people abandon mutual trust as their bond, in favour of protection of themselves against one another in a legal trap?' The idealism of youth makes them want something more than a legal contract, and I emphasize more not less. In the past the religious element probably satisfied this idealism, but the number of church weddings is decreasing and even among those couples who are married in church the reasons are often social rather than religious. There is also the financial side. It has been said that marriage as we know it evolved largely in order that a man could be reasonably sure that a son of his begetting would inherit his wealth. Just another effect of the patriarchal society; everything must pass from father to son.

But, it will be argued, marriage is much more than a legal contract or a financial arrangement. It certainly can be, but frequently these become the predominating factors. Marriage as we know it needs to be looked at carefully and perhaps altered, otherwise it may be doomed. Let us look at the positive values of marriage.

It has often been said that man is an animal that needs to make a pair-bond. The basis for this is usually seen as biological, because of the long period during which human young need to be protected and cared for. Certainly marriage is a convenient way of providing children with the security and affection they need. Possible alternatives will be considered in Chapter 18 on child care. For the moment we will assume that one of the outstanding advantages of marriage is the secure background it provides for children. There is also the privacy and exclusiveness of the relationship between husband and wife. With the complete approval of society they are able to be alone together and to develop a close and rewarding relationship. For the first time in their life they will be allowed to indulge in and experiment with sex. As Bernard Shaw put it: 'Marriage is popular because it combines the maximum of temptation with the maximum of opportunity.'[1]

This is an important side of marriage and we should not scorn it. But in fact marriage is without a rival in offering opportunities for developing a personal relationship and providing a secure harmonious background for children. Unfortunately it frequently fails to do these things. Divorce rates are soaring and this is not just because people are now taking the easy way out. Often it is because we are more honest than our forbears and cannot live in hypocrisy. Divorce is very hard on children but so is an unhappy home which is the scene of constant battles. Children need harmony as well as love and security. Even the security needs to be as much emotional as material and there can be little emotional security in a home without love between the parents.

We need to emphasize the serious and responsible nature of marriage, especially when children are involved. This can only be done by reducing the superficial attractions of, and social pressures towards, marriage. The fuss and the photographs that surround a 'white' wedding, the elevation, for a short time, of the bride into a sort of film star, are attractions that are difficult to resist for a young girl living a dull life. It is a moment of glory. Boys too enjoy the short-lived aura of importance and glamour. They enjoy feeling envied, but unfortunately do not stop to ask why their family and friends, many of whom are already married, should envy them. If marriage is a maturing

[1] *Man and Superman* by Bernard Shaw.

relationship then those who are further along the road should have attained a deeper happiness and have no cause for envy. It is, however, a sad fact that often the glamour and the glory do not last and then it is understandable that those further along the road should envy those who are just starting and therefore still have a chance of succeeding. To be legally and morally bound to someone you do not love is a high price to pay for a day of glory, however memorable it may be. The young should not have to live on memories nor should we try to relive our past glory through them.

Another illusory attraction is freedom. Marriage is seen as a sort of initiation rite which will finally give the couple adult status and free them from the dominance of the parents. It does get them accepted as adults and it frequently gets them away from the parental home, although not necessarily from the parental influence. But the financial pressures of trying to establish a home now begin to shackle them. If children arrive soon, then, unless they are unusually wealthy, their last vestige of freedom vanishes. Marriage is essentially a taking on of responsibilities, and hence a sacrifice of freedom. To enter it expecting a new freedom will soon bring disillusion, which is a poor start for any relationship.

The need for the relief of pressing sexual desire is yet another poor reason for marriage. The young at the height of their sexual powers are told that sex is for 'after you are married'. If they try to practise premarital sex we put as many barriers as possible in their way. They are obliged to try to discover the delights of love in damp fields or in the backs of cars. Not long ago I read an article reviewing the suitability of various makes of cars for love-making and found it very pathetic. That society should reduce something meant to be glorious to furtive fumblings in the backs of cars is tragic. Yet this is what any attempt to follow the dictates of nature reduces our young people to – unless they are willing to marry. Youth is a time of openness, and when they love they want to tell the world about it. The only way they can do this is by marriage and often they are not ready for it.

Teenage marriages are growing in number, yet we know that the younger people are when they marry, the more likely they are to finish in the divorce courts. We have looked at some of the pressures that can push them into a marriage they are not ready for, but there is one reason that overrides all others in 75 per cent of cases. Three out of every four teenage brides are pregnant on their wedding day. That is, or should be, a very sobering figure. Surely everyone will agree that pregnancy is the worst possible reason for marriage. Any couples 'forced' into marriage are bound to feel some degree of resentment. They may even, subconsciously, blame the baby.

If only society will stop persuading its young into marriages that they are not prepared for, then our divorce rate will fall and marriage will become a happier and more worthwhile venture. Before anyone can know if the emotion they are feeling is really love and not just excitement or lust, they need a wide experience of relationships. No one would give sexual desire as the best reason for marriage, but it can be so overwhelming that it blinds us to everything else. If only that desire could be satisfied then a cooler and more realistic appraisal could be made of one's chances of happiness with a particular partner.

There are special hazards in sexual experience before marriage. Pregnancy and venereal disease will be dealt with in later chapters, but there is also an extra risk of emotional damage, because the relationship, lacking respectability and permanence, can be so easily terminated by either partner. This will certainly cause suffering, but less than if a similar break were made after marriage. A broken affair hurts but it is nothing like so destructive as a broken or unhappy marriage.

This is an argument for, not against, marriage, which is in danger of being devalued. We must remove the obstacles which block other outlets for youth's mental and physical as well as sexual energies. If life has a variety of things to offer, then marriage, instead of being the obvious thing, will only be entered into by people who know they want to spend the rest of their days together as well as their nights.

The senior pupils in our schools need to be made to think seriously and honestly about the history and meaning of marriage. Getting married is probably the most serious step they take in the whole of their lives. At present they often enter it with little thought and less preparation. Teachers, together with people such as marriage guidance counsellors, are the ones who must help them to think before they act.

Further Reading

Fletcher, Ronald. *The Family and Marriage in Britain.* (London: Pelican, 1962.)

Winch, R. P. and Goodman, L. W. *Selected Studies in Marriage and the Family.* (New York: Holt Rinehart and Winston, 1953.)

Dicks, H. V. *Marital Tensions.* (London: Routledge and Kegan Paul, 1967.)

Schur, E. M. (ed.). *The Family and the Sexual Revolution.* (London: Allen and Unwin, 1966.)

Goode, W. J. *The Family.* (New York: Prentice Hall, 1964.)

15
Children or Not?

When Ellen Peck's book *The Baby Trap* (see Further Reading) was published in this country, it caused a furore. It is a best seller in America and may well become one over here, so it must meet a need. Until now it has been assumed that the highest duty of every woman was to reproduce the species. In pre-industrial cultures the more children there were the better, for they formed a pool of labour that was vital to survival. Also the heavy infant and early adult mortality rates made a high birth rate necessary even for replacement. But things have changed drastically. Instead of plentiful reproduction being essential to the survival of the human race, it now threatens mankind with destruction. The infant mortality rate has been drastically cut and we all have a much longer life expectation. Unless we can get a compensating cut in the birth rate, then the human race is doomed. It is as serious as that.

> 'Every year there are 17 million more people in the world.
> Every day there are 19 000 more people in the world.
> Every second there are 2.2 more people in the world.'[1]

In prehistoric times it is estimated that the population doubled every 1 000 000 years, by the seventeenth century it was every 1000 years. In the nineteenth century it was doubling every 200 years but by the beginning of the present century it was every 80 years. In 1972 it was doubling every 35 years.

If we couple these figures with our growing awareness of the scarcity of the world's natural resources then it is obvious that drastic action is needed. This, in itself, should be enough to make everyone pause before they start to add to the world's population. There has been talk of legislation to limit the size of families but this, apart from being unenforceable, makes most of us angry because we see it as an infringement of personal liberty. Unless, however, we can find some other way of reducing the birth rate drastically, then something like this will be tried. Surely the obvious way would be to reduce, if possible to eliminate, the unwanted babies. Remember three out of every four teenage brides are pregnant when they marry. Of course many of these babies later become wanted but inherent in this situation is the risk that some will not, and this we cannot afford. We have to ensure that every baby is a wanted baby at the moment of conception. If to the prevention of teenagers' pre-nuptial conceptions we add prevention of all illegitimate babies who are not planned and

[1] Ehrlich, Dr Paul. *The Population Bomb,* London: Ballantine, 1971.

all the unwanted babies conceived in marriage, then we will have made a reduction in the birth rate that may be enough to turn the tide in world prospects. The birth rate in the United Kingdom is already falling but this is only a start. We live on a small, overcrowded island that is far from being self-supporting. Soon the rest of the world will be too busy trying to feed its indigenous populations and will have nothing to spare for us. If we are ever to become anything like self-sufficient then we shall have to reduce our population drastically.

In addition to preventing unwanted conceptions we also need to re-educate ourselves about what constitutes an unwanted baby. Is it enough for a woman to want a baby as a sort of super-doll to play with? Or as a substitute for loneliness or boredom? Even worse are the babies conceived as 'props' to collapsing marriages. Any social worker or marriage guidance counsellor will tell you that babies are more likely to break than make an unstable marriage.

Our society has always expected married couples to have children. Even today we go on expecting young married couples to do so. We may be starting to look askance at big families, but no children at all is a different story. Childless couples are either pitied for their inability, fancied or otherwise, or, if they are known to be childless from choice they are considered selfish. Why children should be looked on as a great blessing, whilst those who choose to deny themselves this blessing are thought of as selfish, is an interesting question.

We are still so influenced by our past, when children were necessary for survival. That mode of thinking needs to be put into reverse. There is a theory that a woman can only fulfil herself by having a child. The proponents of this theory claim biology as their ally. No one ever suggests that men are unfulfilled if they do not father children, yet it is one of their essential functions. We need to make a clearer distinction between childbearing and child rearing. The fact that almost all women are capable of bearing children does not mean that they all want to do so. Until recently a satisfying career, other than that of wife and mother, was a rarity for women. It was, therefore, quite true to say that most of them found their greatest satisfaction in motherhood – what other satisfactions were there? Now the world is beginning to offer them other creative outlets and those who remain childless can fulfil themselves in many ways, as men have done in the past. Probably the great majority of women will still choose to be mothers, but being a mother from choice is a much better thing than becoming one from lack of any satisfying alternative.

Family planners use the phrase 'Every Baby a Wanted Baby' and a very good phrase it is. What needs to be done is to define the word wanted. No woman should have a baby unless, having seen all the opportunities open to her, she knows that that is what she wants more than anything else. This will not only give us a drastic reduction in the world population but it will also ensure that every child gets the best possible start in the world.

Most of the pupils in our secondary schools assume, almost automatically, that they will become parents. It is our job to shake that assumption. Parenthood carries too many responsibilities to be entered into lightly. From the beginning of time childbearing has been a threat hanging over women. Modern contraceptives are removing that threat. If the world is to regain its equilibrium then having a child must become a rare privilege for which we must very carefully prepare ourselves – and our pupils.

We must also make them aware of the other creative roles which are now opening up to women. Why have there been so few first-class women painters, writers, composers, and statesmen? Could it be because all their creativity has been channelled into motherhood? One of the arguments against sexual licence is that progress is only made by men redirecting their sexual energies into other channels. If women are also encouraged to do this then the creative energies available for saving our threatened world will be doubled.

Further Reading

Lorraine, J. A. *Sex and the Population Crises*. (London: Heinemann, 1970.)
Peck, Ellen. *The Baby Trap*. (Bishops Stortford: Heinrich Hanau, 1973.)

16
Contraception

It is all very well to talk about reducing the birth rate and leaving women free to indulge in other creative activities, but this demands either abstention from sex or effective contraception. Abstention must not be ruled out. Consciously undertaken it can be a great spur to other activities by releasing or redirecting sexual energy into different spheres. It must, however, be conscious. Conscious redirection can help to produce excellent creative work, but unconscious repression is more likely to produce warped personalities. Since this conscious absention from sex will be limited to a small minority, it is to contraception that the majority must look.

A popular slogan says 'There is only one way of having a baby but there are eight ways of not having one'. Anyone, but particularly adolescents, indulging in any form of sexual activity that may lead to the penis coming close to the vagina should know how conception takes place and how it can be avoided. They need to know that it is possible for conception to occur without there having been actual intercourse. It is possible for a small drop of semen to leak from an erect penis long before ejaculation. If, as during heavy petting, the penis is near the vaginal orifice then it is possible for the sperms to enter the vagina and swim up through the uterus to the fallopian tubes. Even one drop of semen contains a great number of sperms which are incredibly active and it only takes one sperm to fertilize an ovum. This can happen in a virgin with an unruptured hymen. There must be a hole in the hymen for the menstrual flow to get out, and if it is big enough for that it is big enough to allow the sperms in. The risks of pregnancy from heavy petting are naturally much less than the risks from intercourse, but they do exist and adolescents need to know about them.

Now let us look at these eight ways, starting with the most effective which is, of course, sterilization. Both male and female sterilization is virtually 100 per cent effective. Female sterilization is usually accomplished by cutting and tying the fallopian tubes to prevent the ova and the sperm from meeting (see Figure 3). In some areas it is fairly easy for a woman who has had children to get the operation carried out, in other areas it is more difficult. Sometimes it is done at the same time as another operation or fairly soon after childbirth. It always needs a general anaesthetic. It does not interfere with the menstrual cycle, with the hormone balance, or with the woman's sex life. Male sterilization is similar in that it also calls for the cutting and tying of a tube. This time it

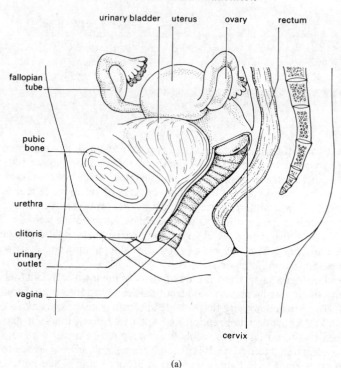

(a)

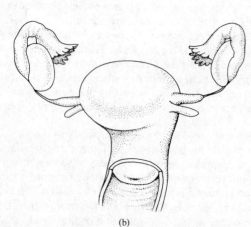

(b)

Figure 3 (a) Female reproductive system; (b) female sterilization by the tube ligation. (From Demarest, R. J. and Sciarra, J. *Conception, Birth and Contraception,* Hodder and Stoughton, 1967.)

is the tube that carries the sperm, the *vas deferens,* hence the name vasectomy (see Figure 4). In a vasectomy the tube is cut between the testicles and the prostate gland so that it does not interfere in any way with the production of semen, nor does it affect the male hormone balance. A man can have an erection and orgasm in exactly the same way as before. His sexual life is quite unaffected by the operation which, as the *vas deferens* is very close to the surface of the body, is a very simple one indeed. It is often performed under a local anaesthetic without admission to hospital. As vasectomy is new many men are unhappy about it; they see it as a threat to their virility, but as more and more of the operations are performed it is gaining in popularity. For couples who are certain that they do not want any further children sterilization can be an ideal solution. It is a purely mechanical method with no interference with the body's chemistry. There is also nothing to remember, nothing to be taken. Once the operation is over the couple can enjoy their sex life without any worries about pregnancies or health risks. But, and it is a but to be taken seriously, the operation must be regarded as irreversible, so anyone undertaking it needs to be sure that they do not want any more children.

The pill works by altering the hormonal balance of the body and thus preventing the release of the egg cell from the ovary. There are various types of pill but they all contain one or both of the female hormones estrogen and progesterone. The most effective pill, which if taken properly will give a virtual 100 per cent protection, is a combination of the two hormones. It is taken for twenty out of every twenty-eight days of the menstrual cycle. The second sequential type consists of estrogen pills followed by progesterone pills. Then there is a progesterone-only type which is thought to be only about 99 per cent effective. The pill does not prevent menstruation but the flow is usually scanty and there is often a decrease in both pre-menstrual tensions and period pains. Much has been written in the popular press about the dangers of the pill, but we must get this in perspective; the danger involved in taking the pill is less than the danger entailed in a normal pregnancy which, in turn, is less dangerous than crossing a busy road. 'It is as dangerous for a New York child to have its tonsils removed as it is for its mother to be on the pill for 160 years.'[1] There are some side effects associated with taking the pill, such as discomfort in the breasts, depression, leg cramps, and weight increase. These are usually due to a hormonal imbalance and can often be corrected by a change of pill. Only 5–15 per cent of women, however, suffer from any side effects; the rest get trouble-free protection from fear of pregnancy. A very few women have medical conditions which make it inadvisable for them to take the pill. Because of this it is only available on a doctor's prescription. Whilst the pill itself is very reliable, the women taking it may be less so and any failures

[1] Malleson, Andrew. *Need Your Doctor Be So Useless?* London: Allen and Unwin, 1970.

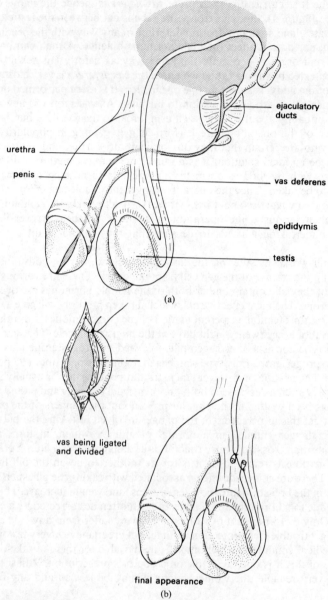

ejaculatory
ducts

urethra

penis

vas deferens

epididymis

testis

(a)

vas being ligated
and divided

final appearance

(b)

Figure 4   (a) Male reproductive system; (b) Male sterilization by vasectomy. (From
Demarest, R. J. and Sciarra, J. op. cit.

attributed to the method usually prove to be due to failure of the woman to take it regularly.

The I.U.D. (intra-uterine device), also known as the coil or loop, is another reasonably effective form of contraception that can be practised by the woman. It is a very old method which Cleopatra is said to have used. Basically it consists of introducing a foreign body into the uterus and leaving it there. In the old days women used things like stones or sponges but today we use plastic or metal coils or loops. They are introduced into the womb through the cervix (see Figure 5) by means of an applicator and can be left in position for years. Apart from some initial discomfort, neither the woman nor the man

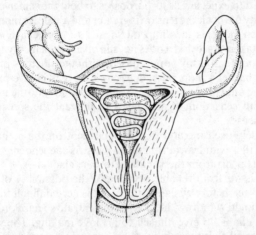

Figure 5   The coil or cap in position. (From Demarest, R. J. and Sciarra, J. op. cit.)

should be conscious of the presence of the I.U.D., although in a few women it gives rise to pain or bleeding and has to be removed. One risk is that the device might be passed out into the lavatory along with stools without the woman realizing that this has happened. She can, and should, check that it is still in position by feeling for the thread which is attached to the device but which is left protruding through the cervix into the vagina. As with sterilization and the pill, the I.U.D. gives constant protection and it causes no break in love-making. It is, however, best suited to women who have had children.

There is not much to choose between the condom and the diaphragm, so far as effectiveness goes. Estimates of their efficiency vary but properly used with a spermicide they give reasonable protection. The diaphragm, or dutch cap, is worn by the woman to close the entrance to the cervix and so prevents sperms entering the uterus. It is a rubber cap with a spring-coil edge which flattens to allow it to be inserted by the woman into the vagina (see Figure 6). The edge should be liberally smeared with a spermicidal jelly. The cap should be put in before intercourse and left in for eight to twelve hours afterwards in order to give any sperms in the vagina time to die. There are many different sizes of cap, and as a correct fit is of vital importance the woman must be fitted with, and shown how to insert, the diaphragm by a doctor. Once it is in place neither partner should be aware of it.

The condom, sheath or french letter is the most widely used of all contraceptives. It is a rubber sheath that is fitted over the erect penis to catch the semen. When used correctly and with a spermicidal cream or jelly it is usually effective. A sheath should only be used once and should be put on before the penis approaches the vagina. Before it is rolled on, the nipple at the end should first be squeezed to expel air, as its purpose is to hold the semen on ejaculation and if it is already full of air the tension is greater and a leakage more likely. After ejaculation when the penis goes limp, the sheath is no longer a tight fit and great care should be taken to see that it does not slip off as the penis is withdrawn. The sheath is cheap and can easily be purchased, without a doctor's prescription, at any chemist or barber's shop, but it does entail a break in love-making since it cannot be put on until the penis is erect. Some men, but by no means all, find that it interferes with sensation. It also helps to prevent the spread of sexually transmitted diseases.

Another widely-used method that is dependent on the man is 'coitus interruptus' or the withdrawal method. This is dependent on the man withdrawing his penis from the vagina before he ejaculates. As a contraceptive method it is far from reliable because of the possibility of a leakage of sperm-laden semen before ejaculation. Also it is very difficult for a man to be sure when he should withdraw. He has to concentrate so hard on getting out in time that he is unable to give himself to his love-making. The woman too is continually worried about his ability to withdraw in time and she also is tense. Love-making should give joy and release from tension and the withdrawal method prevents this. It is thought to be the cause of emotional stress and may even lead to the breakdown of the marriage or mental ill-health. It is not a method which should be used regularly.

The shops are full of spermicidal jellies, creams, foams, and suppositories which claim to kill sperms. Some of them claim to be effective if used alone but no family-planning expert would accept this claim. Used together with the sheath or the condom they are very useful indeed, but should never be relied on alone. Most of the foams are sold with an applicator in order that the foam can be inserted as far into the vagina as possible, in the region of the cervix (see Figure 7). Spermicides can also play a useful role in preventing the spread of sexually transmitted diseases.

The safe period or rhythm method is the only form of contraception that some people are allowed by their religion to use. As this safe period is far from safe it is not a method recommended for people who really do not want a child. It is also a very difficult method to use. For people with irregular periods it is almost impossible and this rules it out for most adolescents. A woman

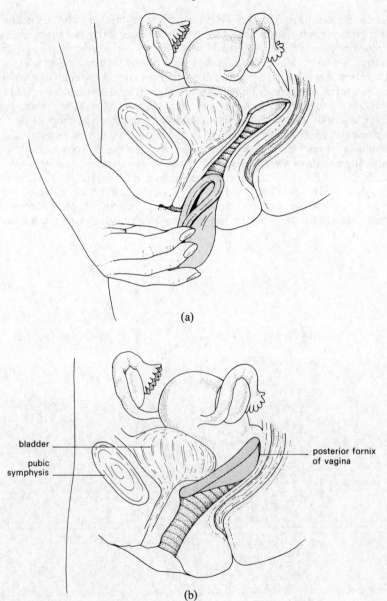

Figure 6 (a) Insertion of the cap; (b) The cap in position. (From Demarest, R. J. and Sciarra, J. op. cit.)

whose periods have settled down into a regular rhythm and who wishes to use this method must start by taking her temperature regularly every morning and recording it on a chart. About mid-way between periods the ovaries produce an egg and on this day (ovulation day) the temperature usually rises slightly. If ovulation is regular over a period of six months then the woman can begin to calculate her safe period. First, she must allow at least one day before and one day after ovulation day as it can vary, then she must allow at least three other days before the first ovulation day to allow any sperms in her body to die plus three days after the last ovulation day to allow time for the ovum to die. If ovulation takes place on the fourteenth day then the thirteenth, fourteenth, and fifteenth days must be counted as possible ovulation days. Days 10, 11, and 12 must be avoided to give the sperm time to die and days 16, 17, and 18 to allow the ovum to die. As days 1 to 7 will be days of menstruation when many people have aesthetic objections to intercourse, although there is no medical basis for this, then the only days on which it is reasonably safe to have

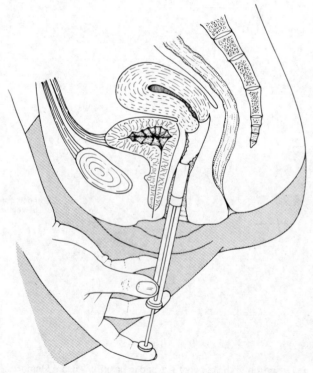

Figure 7   Foam applicator. (From Demarest, R. J. and Sciarra, J. op. cit.)

intercourse are 8, 9, 10, and 19 to 28 (see Table 2). This is assuming a regular twenty-eight day cycle with ovulation also occurring regularly and very few women have this. Periods coming more frequently than every twenty-eight days and any irregularity will reduce greatly the number of days available for intercourse. Furthermore we must remember that the menstrual cycle is very easily disturbed by illness, emotional upset or even a change of life style. Another difficulty is that sexual desire does not confine itself within the limits of safety and there is at least half the month when the couple will have to resist temptation. This is also true of the six months' preparatory period. For anyone whose religion does not allow other methods it is far better than nothing, but it is fraught with difficulties and needs the support of a religious belief if it is to be used.

Table 2 Safe period

Menstrual period	Safe period ?	Days for sperm to die	Possible ovulation days	Days for ovum to die	Safe period ?
1 2 3 4 5 6	7 8 9	10 11 12	13 14 15	16 17 18	19 20 21 22 23 24 25 26 27 28

A knowledge of the various methods of contraception is not all that young people need, but it is essential. They need also to know that advice is available to anyone over sixteen years (and most centres do not ask for a birth certificate) and where the centres are in their areas. The general practitioner is one source of help and advice, but for those adolescents who are afraid to go to him, because they feel that he will tell their parents, there is usually a clinic run by the Local Authority, the Family Planning Association, or the Brook Advisory Centre. It cannot be emphasized too much that such advice is confidential. Every couple should consider the methods available, decide which will suit them best, and seek advice if they need it.

The moral issues involved should be discussed but never made an excuse for withholding or falsifying information. If there is one sexual crime about which all people agree it is that of bringing into the world a child that is unwanted and ill-prepared for. Nothing must stop us from doing all we can to prevent this.

Further Reading

Cartwright, Ann. *Parents and Family Planning Services.* (London: Routledge and Kegan Paul, 1970.)

Demarest, R. J. and Sciarra, J. *Conception, Birth, Contraception.* (London: Hodder and Stoughton, 1967.)

Family Planning in Britain. Office of Health Economics, 1972.

17
Abortion

No one likes the thought, or the fact, of an abortion, least of all the woman who undergoes it and the medical staff who perform it. The sooner the numbers of abortions performed in the world are drastically reduced the better. It is unlikely that we will ever be able to dispense with the operation completely for medical reasons, but we should be able to make it a rare operation. Everyone will agree about the desirability of this but not about the ways in which it can be accomplished.

First of all we must realize that by far the greatest number of abortions are natural ones. Natural abortion usually occurs when something has gone wrong with the process of fertilization or implantation.

> 'Errors such as these are mostly self-eliminating during the first two weeks of pregnancy, and both the mistake and its erasure pass unsuspected. Yet the number is undoubtedly high, not less than a third of all *conceptions*. More is known concerning natural abortions that occur at some later stage when the event causes concern and usually medical examination.'[1]

Let us look at this approximate figure of one-third – 33·3 per cent of all conceptions ending as natural abortions. It is impossible for accurate figures to be produced but all the experts put the figure very high. The important thing is that most of these abortions take place very early in pregnancy and are seldom recognized as what they are. Either the foetus is passed out during a particularly heavy menstrual period or it is flushed down the lavatory. It is part of nature's normal policy of the survival of the fittest. The mother suffers no ill-effects, either physical, mental, or emotional. Not for her the feelings of guilt and depression that are said to dog the steps of her less fortunate sister who needs assistance with her abortion. No priest holds up his hands in horror, no doctor refuses to co-operate. It is a simple, natural affair.

Unfortunately nature sometimes fails to rectify her mistakes at this early stage, even when all is not well with the foetus. Thus we get births of deformed and handicapped children. Even at this late stage nature would like to remedy her mistake by an early death, but man refuses to allow the natural process of survival of the fittest to apply; medical science steps in to ensure that babies now live who would formerly have died. Many of them live most of their lives

[1] Berrill, N. J. *The Person in the Womb*. Dodd, Mead and Co., 1968, page 151.

in institutions, others place an almost intolerable burden on their families. Some live to reproduce and pass on a very doubtful genetic inheritance. Of course they frequently generate love and unselfish caring in those around them, but they can also cause frustration and weary imprisonment for their families. Some of those who are kept alive in this way by medical science do enjoy life, others seem to find it a burden. Where we draw the line depends on our philosophy of life, but it is time for us to face the question. We need to look ahead to the results our present behaviour will have on future generations. A sweeping sentimental generalization that all life is sacred can only be logically maintained by an out-and-out vegan-pacifist. The rest of us must draw the line somewhere and we need to ask ourselves whether life, any kind of life, is enough or whether the quality of that life needs to be considered. Dr Berrill says:[2]

'The human right is the right of every individual to be born without handicap in mind or body, to be nurtured in every way during infancy and childhood so that full development is achieved and to maintain the integrity of the person thereafter.'

Could any teacher ask for a more fascinating subject for discussion by senior pupils?

We must remember that medical science is now keeping alive many people who would not have been allowed by nature to reach maturity. Now these people are not only being kept alive but are reproducing and no one knows what the effect of this will be on the population at large. Let us look at one or two of the examples Dr Berrill gives:

'Before insulin was discovered a few decades ago as a means of counteracting the sugar metabolism deficiency that we know as diabetes, women with hereditary diabetes did not live to produce children. Now they do so freely, and the present population in the United States is said to contain some fifty million people with this deficiency, most of them able at some time to pass on their abnormality to another and larger generation. With P.K.U. (phenylketonuria, a disease of babies which causes mental deficiency if untreated) a similar situation is beginning to arise. Current practices indicate that patients with P.K.U. may not have to be on treatment after childhood. [But] ... should they eventually marry and bear children each one will require treatment throughout her pregnancy. What we are doing for the individual patient may ultimately do considerable harm to the next generation and eventually even to the race. At any rate, the general prospect should cause any couple about to get married and any married couple considering having children to look at each other as prospective parents in the light of their own characteristics and their

---

[2] Ibid.

hereditary background. There are risks that may be taken and some that should not.'

There is discussion group material here to keep a class busy for some time and we must not limit these discussions to academic sixth-forms. These are matters that concern us all, and properly handled they can be made alive and interesting to non-academics of fourteen and over. They are not only relevant to their lives but can be seen to be relevant.

The point I have been trying to make is that nature usually disposes of the products of an imperfect conception early and easily. Is it so terrible for man to step in where nature fails (it is now often possible to detect these abnormalities early in pregnancy), allow a woman to escape from the nightmare of bringing a deformed child into the world, and at the same time protect the genetic quality of the human race? Ask your class what they think.

But the risk of a deformed child is only one reason for abortion. The British Abortion Act of 1967[3] lists four such reasons. It says that abortion may be legally performed where:

1. the continuance of the pregnancy would involve risk to the life of the pregnant woman greater than if the pregnancy were terminated;
2. the continuance of the pregnancy would involve risk of injury to the physical or mental health of the pregnant woman greater than if the pregnancy were terminated;
3. the continuance of the pregnancy would involve risk of injury to the physical or mental health of the existing child(ren) of the family of the pregnant woman greater than if the pregnancy were terminated;
4. there is a substantial risk that if the child were born it would suffer from such physical or mental abnormalities as to be seriously handicapped.'

We have dealt with the last one; let us now examine the other three. The first condition is the one that gains the most widespread agreement. Here it is not a question of taking a life (if it ever is) but a matter of choosing between two lives. One is a full human being with responsibilities, able usually to produce another baby within a short time. She is surely due for the consideration we should accord to all humans. The baby has the potential that will enable it to become a full human being but it has not yet reached that status, it has no responsibilities, and without its mother its chances of becoming a valuable human being are reduced. It is a choice between the actual and the potential and only a very few people would hesitate when called on to decide.

It is the second and third clauses of the Act that have given rise to the greatest controversy and which are open to various interpretations. Let us take clause two first. Injury to the physical health of the woman is fairly straightforward and is really an extension of clause one unless we include the physical strain and damage to health that may be caused by caring for a

[3] The Abortion Act, H.M.S.O., 1967.

large family. If the family is poor as well as large the mother may well be little more than a drudge and her diet inadequate. Every additional child is an extra mouth to feed, which usually means less food for the mother. Also each child increases the amount of work she has to do and constitutes a drain on her physical resources. It can be an even greater strain on her emotional and mental resources. There is a limit to the amount of ourselves any of us can give without suffering damage. This is true of physical effort, mental interest, and emotional involvement. Children need physical care, they need to have an interest taken in all their doings and, above all, they need love and emotional security. We all vary in the amount we have to give but we all have a limit beyond which we should not be asked to go. A woman might have abundant resources for one child, an adequate supply for two, but if she is asked to spread her resources over three children then maybe she is being asked to give too much and the result will be injury to her physical, mental – and I would like to add emotional – health. It will also result in injury to the existing child(ren). If the amount of food that is barely adequate for two children has to be spread over three then it obviously results in an inadequate diet for all three. What is true of food is true of mental interest and love. These things are not inexhaustible, some people have a much greater reservoir of them than others, but we all have our breaking point. Those who look on mother love as a bottomless well are usually men, women without children, or those screened from reality by wealth.

No woman should ever be expected to bear a child that she feels she cannot care for properly. It is she who carries the child, gives birth to it, and, in our present society, gives up years of her life to its care. Yet the laws and the religious pronouncements on the subject all come from men. The time has come for women to say, 'We will decide'. People talk about 'abortion on demand' with horror as though all the pregnant women in the world would rush for abortions the moment they were able to. Yet these are the people who talk a great deal about the sanctity of motherhood and mother love. Where is their faith in that mother love? They say that women are biologically designed to bear children and that in doing so they will find their greatest fulfilment. If they really believe this then they have no need to fear liberal abortion laws, they can leave it to nature.

One interesting argument used against allowing the woman to decide is that some women are selfish and immature and would have an abortion to avoid responsibility. These are the very women who should have abortions. Any child born to a selfish and immature woman is going to have a poor time of it. Only a very naïve man would believe that childbirth would either remove selfishness or add maturity.

It is suggested that women who have abortions will suffer from guilt and depression. If they do it is the fault of some sections of society. We are back to expectation. What we are induced to expect, that we often experience. Those who have natural abortions do not feel guilty or depressed because no one tells them that they should. Anti-abortionists also stress the risks of abortion and of course they exist, but they are less than the dangers of a full-term pregnancy. Such risks as there are can be reduced by early abortion. The further advanced the pregnancy, the greater the risk involved.

The methods used to induce abortions vary according to the area in which it is done. Here are the methods used in Aberdeen Hospitals:

Length of Pregnancy (weeks)	Method
6–12	Suction curettes (general anaesthetic not essential before 8th week)
12–20	Protoglandins infusion to induce uterine contractions, or injection through abdomen into uterus to remove amniotic fluid and replace it with normal saline, thus killling

This should make it obvious that, if possible, all abortions should take place before the end of the third month. Nothing will do more to bring about this desirable state of affairs than a system which allows every woman who wants an abortion to have one immediately she suspects that she is pregnant. At present women are hesitant and worried. They are often not sure whether they would qualify under the Act and because they are afraid of being refused they never ask. Others ask and are refused. Yet others leave it longer than they should because they are made to feel guilty by society.

So far we have only discussed legal abortions but there are many women refused by the official system, or afraid of it, who resort to illegal abortions. The Abortion Act came into being to save women from these back street abortionists and it has certainly reduced them in number. But until legal, comparatively risk-free abortions are available for all women who want them, desperate women will resort to other means. The wealthy can buy their way into sterile comfortable nursing homes but the poor woman must either try to induce it herself or find a back street practitioner. In the latter two cases the risk to the woman's life and health is enormous and no civilized country should allow its women to take such risks.

The climate of opinion in this country changed enough to allow the passage of the 1967 Act. It will, in time, change to allow abortions to all women who feel unprepared for the terrific task of childbearing and motherhood. The only uncertainty is how much time will be needed. We need to make it as short as possible. There are far too many people in the world and the first step towards reducing them must be the prevention of the birth of unwanted children. Abortion is a poor method of doing this and should only be used when other methods have failed, but it is an essential safety net.

Minds do change. Much of the present objection to abortion comes from

organized religion which tries to give the impression that it is upholding values
proved by time. This is not so. Let me quote Dr Berrill again:[4]

> '... we are coping not with crude medieval attitudes but with harsh laws
> laid down by our much more recent mid-Victorian predecessors. Until then
> the general rule was that of the ancient Greeks. Aristotle, who
> recommended abortion when couples already have children in excess,
> stated that life did not begin until the "quickening" and so abortion was per-
> missible during the preceding months. More precisely, abortion was
> allowable during the first forty days for a male infant and eighty days for
> females. How anyone could know the sex of the foetus at such an early
> stage we are not told. But this forty-day, eighty-day rule was preserved in
> the Justinian Code a thousand years after Aristotle ... medieval English
> common law permitted abortion on demand provided it was accomplished
> before quickening. The pregnant woman, even if married, was the sole per-
> son whose consent or request was required. This remained the law of
> England until 1803. .... Even then the new laws merely distinguished
> between an abortion before and after quickening. Not until 1861 did
> England pass legislation without respect to the time of gestation.'

If the laws against abortion in England are only just over 100 years old, then
the greatest weight of tradition is on the side of those who want abortion, at least
in the early stages of pregnancy, to rest entirely with the mother.

There is a Swedish pill known as the M pill or menstruation pill which interferes with the production of the female hormone progesterone and prevents
the implantation of the fertilized egg in the wall of the uterus. There is also the
morning-after pill. Something along these lines which a woman can take
when she has had unprotected intercourse, or take once a month in order to
bring on a menstrual period without knowing whether she is pregnant or not,
should lower the need for abortion. With good education, freely available contraceptives and something in the nature of an M or morning-after pill as a final
line of defence, the only women who will need abortions will be those who are
found to have foetal abnormalities or whose own health is suffering as a result
of pregnancy. This result should please everyone.

Further Reading

Berrill, N. T. *The Person in the Womb.* (New York: Dodd, Mead and Co., 1968.)
Horobin, G. W. *Experience with Abortion.* (Cambridge University Press, 1973.)
Simms, Madeleine and Hindell, Keith. *Abortion Law Reformed.* (London: Peter
Owen, 1971.)

[4] Ibid. pages 157–8.

18
Parenthood

So far we have concentrated on how to avoid the birth of unwanted babies; now we must look at the needs of wanted ones. It is not enough (although it is the greatest single need) for the prospective parents to want the child. They must be prepared to take care of it physically, psychologically, and materially. No one is allowed to drive a car until they have taken lessons, passed a test, and obtained a licence. They must also have reached a certain age. Being a good parent requires far more skill than driving a car, yet prospective parents have little opportunity for training themselves for their new role. In some areas quite a lot of help is given to parents during the ante- and post-natal periods and this is invaluable. What we need, however, is education aimed at showing young people just what is involved in bringing a child into the world and caring for it before they make the decision to have a child. This would make for more responsible parenthood and a better start in life for the child. It is no good waiting until the child is on the way before showing them just what it needs in the way of emotional and physical care. At this stage, if they find they have not got the resources, their only alternatives are an abortion or an inadequately nurtured child with overstrained parents. There is only one place where education can be sure of reaching everyone and that is at school. So it is once again up to the teachers and this is a fascinating subject which can generate a great deal of interest in a fifteen to sixteen year-old class.

Some schools have already seen this need and are meeting it, others are dealing with certain facets of it. What should we teach? First we must start by looking at the needs of the baby. The physical needs are simpler so let us start there. This does not mean lessons in how to bath the baby or what strength of milk mixture it needs; these things if taught now will be forgotten and anyway they are dealt with expertly by the health visitor and midwife during the ante- and post-natal periods. It does mean looking at the material needs of the baby, such as pram, cot, nappies, and clothes, and costing these. So many young parents are quite unprepared for the simple financial cost of the baby. No one should have a child without knowing that they have the money to meet its physical needs. Posh prams with fancy covers are quite unnecessary, but a pram of some sort is needed, and so are a lot of other things. It may seem mercenary to emphasize this, but money, or rather the lack of it, can lead to a great deal of strife. If a young couple without children can only just make ends meet, then they will have to make material sacrifices if they want to have children. If they want children enough then they will make the sacrifices gladly. but the cost should be assessed beforehand or the baby will suffer. Perhaps a little practical mathematics could be done on this. It might not help towards 'O' levels but it would help towards a happy life.

If the material costs are high then the psychological and emotional costs are still higher. There is, however, one big difference, in this sphere the baby will give as much as it gets. We cannot and should not expect material rewards from our children, but the love and attention we give them is usually returned with interest. Even so a young baby does make tremendous demands on both its parents, particularly the mother. First she has the nine long months of pregnancy. For many this is a joy and they are proud of their increasing girth, but others worry about it and try to hide it. Why? If a baby is really wanted should the mother be ashamed of being pregnant? Has the father any influence here? These are questions to be asked by us, but answered by the class. Then there is childbirth itself. Is this something to be looked forward to with joy or is it an ordeal to be dreaded? How much truth is there in old wives' tales? Why do older women like to tell gory stories of their parturition? Let some members of the class go to ante-natal clinics and classes to find out what young mothers feel and report back. Get one or two to study psychoprophylaxis, which is a terrible name for a simple and easy way of helping women to enjoy childbirth. Its chief exponent in this country is Erna Wright, and her book *The New Childbirth* (see Further Reading) is a clear exposition of the method. Psychoprophylaxis has reduced the pain involved in labour. It is still hard work, but now it is rewarding work, quite different from the agonizing experiences of our grandparents. Whilst no girl should ever be allowed to have a child she does not want, equally no girl should be prevented from having a child by fear of childbirth. Fear is usually due to ignorance and our task is to remove the ignorance. If your local authority does not run classes in psychoprophylaxis then contact the nearest branch of the National Childbirth Trust. Fathers too have a role to play in this; their co-operation is vital if the full benefit is to be obtained from psychoprophylaxis training. All classes discussing these matters should be mixed as it still takes two sexes to make a baby and to rear it.

Another subject for discussion should be where the mother should have the baby. Usually there is little choice, for nearly all babies today, certainly all first babies, are delivered in hospital. During the past thirty years there has been a great shift from home to hospital deliveries. This was so that help could be at hand if anything went wrong and so that every precaution could be taken against infection. These are both very laudable motives and they have helped to reduce the maternal mortality rate but we seem to be in danger of treating childbirth as an illness. It is not; it is a natural process and the natural place to have it is at home. Britain has the most highly trained midwives in the world; they are quite capable of conducting normal deliveries at home. If anything goes wrong flying squads can be there in minutes. Most of these arrangements are made by men; any woman who has had one baby in hospital and one at home will tell you that home delivery is incomparably better for both mother and child. The mother has the security of her home and family, everything is friendly and personal, above all she remains herself. Even in the best of hospitals it is not possible to match these conditions. At home there is quietness and mother and baby are able to work out their own routine of sleep, feeding, and cuddling without having to fit into tight ward schedules. Also the dangers of cross-infection are greatly reduced. American women are starting to protest against being forced into hospital. British women (with the exception of those in the high-ish category) need to do so too before we lose our wonderful midwives. A final benefit of home confinement for second or subsequent babies is that the mother does not have to leave her other infants and we know what damage such separations can cause.

Once the mother is home, or the midwife has ceased attendance, the young couple are left alone with their baby. This can be both an exciting and a frightening experience. Babies are so small and vulnerable and there are so many theories about their upbringing that young parents get very confused. The health visitor is the person who can be relied on to give expert help and guidance at this time. She will visit the baby as soon as the midwife ceases her visits and will call as often as is needed until the child starts school.

Looking after babies can be physically exhausting; there is a lot of washing and, unless the baby is breast fed, a lot in the way of preparation of feeds, sterilization of bottles, etc. At first the baby will waken frequently for feeding; its stomach is small and it needs food little and often. All attempts to force babies into regular feeding schedules merely result in upset and frustration for both mother and child but, left alone, the baby will soon settle down into its own rhythm. However for the first few weeks there will be night feeds to be given and the lack of sleep involved in this, plus the extra work and responsibility during the day, can be very exhausting. Would-be parents should be aware of this before they decide to have a child. We can awaken this awareness.

Another thing that needs to be openly discussed is breast feeding. It used to be the only effective way of feeding, but in the last twenty years artificial foods have been produced which are able to nourish a young baby satisfactorily. These artificial foods contain all the nutrients needed and any mother who is unable to breast feed or who does not choose to do so need not worry about her child's nutrition. She must remember, however, that a child gets much more than milk from a breast feed. It is cuddled close to the warm bare skin of its mother and that close warm contact is of vital importance to the child's development. A baby who is held close to its mother's body whilst it is fed from the bottle will not be deprived of this essential comfort, but one whose bottle is propped up in the pram will be emotionally deprived as well as in danger of choking. Another advantage of breast milk is that it contains antibodies which will protect the child from some diseases during the first vital months and these cannot be included in artificial foods. Also breast milk is cheaper, there is no preparation, no sterilization of bottles, and it is always there when you need it. And as one doctor put it 'the cat can't get at it'. Some mothers do not breast feed their babies because they want to feel free to go out. After all, Father or Granny can give the baby a bottle. This is a reasonable viewpoint but it might be worth considering a mixture of breast and bottle feeding. There is an emotional satisfaction in breast feeding for both mother and child. The saddest reason for mothers refusing to breast feed is that they feel too bashful. This is a result of our society's flaunting of the breast as a sex symbol. It makes girls ashamed of breast feeding unless they are alone, which makes life difficult. Perhaps the bras that the militant 'women's lib' types have burnt will serve a useful purpose after all. If we stop flaunting the breast as a sex symbol it may come back into its own as a milk-producing organ. Our babies would benefit from this.

Food, warmth, love, and security are essential to all babies but they are such demanding creatures that they need something more and that is mental stimulation. They need to be talked to, sung to, and played with from a very early age. Modern research shows that the child responds to its mother's voice even before it is born. Once it is out in the world it needs all the stimulation it can get. This does not mean that we should try to force our children as though they were hot-house plants; this could only do damage. In fact it has been suggested that it is vital that a child does not miss out on any of its developmental steps. At the Institute for Learning Disability (*sic!*) in America they are working on the possibility of a link between crawling and reading:

'... hundreds of children who were failing to learn to read by look-say, phonetics or whatever, have been made into good readers by getting them down on their knees and having them creep for ten or fifteen minutes a day for weeks. The theory is that if these children had crept properly and long enough as babies, their side-to-side eye movements, combined with the symphony of muscular co-ordination, would have properly prepared their brains for readiness to read. These were the children who had readily accepted the hands of adults who too soon and too readily offered to help them walk. Timing is all-important. Each phase of each step depends on the previous one having been properly and fully experienced.'[1]

It is not necessary to accept the link between crawling and reading, which is an interesting idea still being investigated, but we must accept the underlying concept of allowing children to develop at their own pace and in their own way. There is always the danger of using a child to 'keep up with the Joneses'. If Janet next door walks at 12 months then we do our best to urge Jane to walk at $11\frac{1}{2}$ months. It might make us feel good but what effect does it have on Jane? We must not use our children to boost our morale or push us a rung

[1] Berrill, N. J. op. cit., page 142.

further up the competitive ladder. Our job is to provide, not to push. If we provide a variety of stimuli the child can be trusted to use what is appropriate to its stage of development. A rich environment will enable it to evolve a wide and well-balanced support system.

In the first few months the child is dependent on its mother or mother-substitute but as it grows its horizons widen to take in the rest of the nuclear family and later the extended family, school, and community. What sort of home situation is best for the child? What will provide the most secure base? Until recently the answer was unquestionably the family. Most people would still say the family, but what do we mean by the family? The modern family unit is so very different from that of our grandparents. The small nuclear family isolated from grandparents and other relatives forms a close, rather intense unit. In a family of two parents and two children it is easy for the children to become almost submerged by adult pressures and expectations. The large families of the past were protected from over-mothering or fathering by sheer weight of numbers. The parents had to spread their energies more widely, which helped to make them less intense and possessive. The relationship was also diluted by grandparents, aunts, uncles, and cousins. Our present small family is an intense hot-house which forms a forcing atmosphere for children. Is it any wonder that they rebel, or that mother, having lavished all her energies on them for years, feels lost and useless when they grow up and leave home? Something must be done to relieve this intense pressure, to free both mother and children to develop their individual personalities. Whether we can do this by going back to the old extended family or whether we have to evolve some new system is something that will have to be worked out. It has been suggested by 'women's lib' that in some cases father should take over the care of the child whilst mother goes out to work. Certainly in some families the man is better equipped by temperament than the woman to cope with small children, but women who claim that they find the home a prison should not expect to escape at the cost of shutting their husbands up in their stead. Perhaps they could share it in, say, yearly stints. A few people have tried to overcome the problem by setting up communities. Some of these have flourished, but many have run into difficulties so great that they have had to disband. The play-group and nursery school provision, which is increasing fast, is giving a degree of freedom to women as well as providing a stimulating environment for the children. These groups for young children must be kept small and it is essential that every child in them gets plenty of individual affection and attention. Research done on children in institutions has produced some horrifying results:

'In the particular foundling home under study, the developmental quotient of the babies, whose mothers were too poor to keep them but who were presumably normal, fell from an initial 131 at the age of two or three months to a mere 72 at the end of the year. Yet in a nursery attached to a women's prison, where the babies were cared for every day by mothers who were mentally retarded women, delinquent minors and psychopaths, the babies' developmental quotient rose from 97 at age two or three months to an average of 112 at four or five months and finally settled back to 100 by the end of their first year, which was the norm for their age. Being fed from a bottle and kept clean, or even being breast fed, is not enough. Infants need full-time love and care from someone, not necessarily the biological mother, or they will either perish or grow up emotionally and to some extent mentally crippled.'[2]

A woman is more than a mother, she has a mind and a body as well as feelings. Small children are emotionally satisfying but they are not mentally stimulating. If a woman is forced to spend all her time at home with small children she may well get frustrated and resentful. This will do her relationship with her children nothing but harm. But in helping the mother we must be careful not to harm the children. Father taking a greater share of child care helps and it also enriches his life. Employers could do a great deal by providing part-time work for mothers that would fit in with nursery and school hours and holidays. Perhaps best of all would be an encouragement of a community spirit in which young mothers could get together to help each other and which might be able to fill the gap left in the lives of middle-aged women by the independence of their own children. Older people are usually very good with children and many of them have time and energy to spare. Could not they help with the care of the very young? Our pupils will be facing these problems in a few years' time. If we can start them thinking about it now, maybe they will find solutions that have so far evaded us.

The problems of the small nuclear family can seem difficult but they are nothing compared to the hurdles facing the one-parent family. Unmarried mothers, widows, widowers, the divorced, and separated people often find it almost impossible to provide both a steady income and a secure home. They need all the help the community can give. In particular we need to help the unmarried mother. She may be a courageous woman who has decided that she wants a child without a husband and feels that she can provide that child with all it needs. Such a woman deserves our admiration and our help. Usually, however, the unmarried mother has become pregnant by accident. She has not married the father, either because he was unwilling or already married, or because she decided not to make a second mistake by marrying for expediency. Many girls in this position either have abortions or place the child for adoption. Some decide to abide by the consequences of their action and keep the child; they often have strong maternal instincts. If they have a family to give help and support, then their way may be reasonably smooth, but if their families cast them off then they have a difficult time and, more important, so do the children. It has been said that there are no illegitimate children, only

[2] Ibid. page 138.

illegitimate parents. Could we not dispense with the word altogether? Young girls who become pregnant are often looking for the love and affection they themselves missed as children. They may try to find that love and security in their child; let us not make it too difficult for them. At the same time we need to try to make our pupils see what a tremendous responsibility we take on when we decide to bring another life into being. Such decisions should be made with as much forethought and knowledge as possible. We owe this to the children of the future and we can only do it through educating their parents.

Further Reading

Bowlby, John. *Child Care and the Growth of Love.* (London: Pelican, 1965.)

Caplan, Gerlad. *An Approach to Community Mental Health.* (London: Tavistock, 1969, Chapters 3 and 4.)

Consumers' Assocation. *Pregnancy Month by Month,* 1968.

Demarest, R. J. and Sciarra, J. *Conception, Birth, Contraception.* (London: Hodder and Stoughton, 1969.)

Wright, Erna. *The New Childbirth.* (New York: Tandem, 1964.)

19
Sexually Transmitted Diseases

The label Sexually Transmitted Diseases is rapidly replacing the term Venereal Diseases as a way of describing those diseases spread by intimate bodily contact. This is largely because in the past the term venereal (named after Venus the goddess of love) has only been applied to a small group of diseases, the chief of which are syphilis and gonorrhoea. It is now realized that a much wider group are spread by sexual contact and it is also hoped that a new name will help to remove the shame which prevents sufferers from seeking treatment.

The complete list of ailments that can be passed on by sexual contact would be as long as a list of all the infectious and contagious diseases afflicting mankind, for the closer you get to a person suffering from any disease the more likely you are to get it, and does anything bring people into closer contact than love-making? This applies to the common cold and measles just as much as it does to syphilis or gonorrhoea. It is possible for us to cause disease in our partner even though we may not be conscious of it ourselves. Our bodies are full of bacteria which may be roughly divided into three groups. The first, such as the group of bacteria in the intestines which help in the process of digestion, are definitely beneficial. Then there is a group which seems neither to help nor harm us. They are capable of producing illness or reaction in some people but very often they can reside in our bodies with no ill-effects, either because we have built up a resistance to them or because we are not allergic to them. These can be passed on to another person who may be either allergic or without resistance to them. Non-specific urethritis may come into this category, but we will discuss that later. The third group of organisms are those that are definitely harmful to the host as well as to the partner. In this category are syphilis and gonorrhoea.

If we catch a cold or a sore throat from kissing an infected person we are not immediately covered with shame or embarrassment. Yet if it is discovered that we have syphilis or gonorrhoea we may be treated as lepers or criminals. It is a sign of improvement that it is only 'we may be'; twenty years ago, or even ten, we definitely would have been. Is it largely because kissing is socially acceptable whilst intercourse still is not? Where are we going to draw the line?

For so long the two letters V.D. have been used as a threat, a sword of Damocles that would fall upon young people who followed the instincts which nature gave them but which older people were determined they should not enjoy. That sword of Damocles used to bring with it disaster, social and physical. The social disaster is rapidly disappearing and we need to do all we can to hasten its departure, for it is fear of social ostracism that makes people hide, sometimes even from themselves, the fact that they may have the disease. This results in their refusing to seek treatment and so the physical results do bring disaster. Let us make no mistake about it, untreated venereal diseases do a great deal of harm and can result in death. *But* early treatment can cure them completely. Society can commit no greater crime than to make young people afraid or unaware of these diseases to such an extent that they fail to get early treatment. Treatment is available in all our large centres of population. It is free and confidential. It is effective. But these great benefits are to some extent nullified by the difficulty of getting treatment. Young people just do not know where to go and it is often difficult to find out. Usually even the telephone directory is useless. You can look up venereal disease or sexually transmitted disease and find nothing. Sometimes it masquerades under the euphemism 'special clinic' and sometimes it is just an extension from a general hospital number. The last of these is good in that it treats sexually transmitted diseases as it does other diseases, but it is of no help to a frightened teenager. Is it any wonder that so many people do not seek treatment, or at least not successfully, when advertising is usually restricted to public lavatories and looking for a telephone number is like looking for a needle in a haystack? At present only the intelligent, unusually determined, or well-taught individuals ever succeed in getting the treatment that is available. We must drastically increase our advertising of these clinics and bring it into the open where it will be seen. How many people use the public lavatories in their home area? Then we must list clinics in the telephone directory under every conceivable name. The cost of a few extra entries would be paid for by even one extra case of syphilis treated in its primary stage. Above all we must make sure *no* child leaves school without being aware of the way in which these diseases are passed on, of their signs and symptoms, of the fact that, treated early, they can be cured, that treatment is free and *confidential,* that they will not be made to feel like criminals, and of where and when they should go for treatment.

There is still a lingering belief that syphilis and gonorrhoea can be caught from lavatory seats and it must be made absolutely clear that this does not happen. Both the gonococcus and the spirochaete (the causative organisms) die within a few seconds of being exposed to the air. They are passed on only through intimate bodily contact. This is usually intercourse, but it can also be homosexual contact.

A lot of people are hazy about the signs and symptoms of these diseases and, particularly in the case of women, this is not surprising as they are not always easy to define. Let us take syphilis first, not because it is the most common but because it is the most dangerous. Taken on a world-wide basis there has been a steep rise in the number of reported cases of syphilis, but in Britain this rise has been both slower and smaller. There is still a high level of the disease amongst seamen and an increasing number of homosexuals are being diagnosed as syphilitic. Far more men are affected than women. Syphilis is divided into three stages, each with its own signs and symptoms. *The primary stage* consists of a painless sore, or chancre, at the site of infection. This is usually on the penis in the male and so is easily visible, but in the female the chancre may well be situated high in the vagina or in the cervix, so that it is not visible and often goes unnoticed. Occasionally the chancre is situated on the mouth, the organism having entered through an abrasion in the skin or mucous membrane. These chancres appear within three weeks of infection and are highly contagious. But even if untreated they will go away in a few weeks. *The secondary stage* is heralded by a faint painless rash which may cover the whole body. It is easily confused with adolescent skin troubles. The rash may or may not be accompanied by a slightly raised temperature and a sore throat. It usually appears two to three months after infection. As with the chancre it will eventually go away even if it is untreated. *The tertiary stage* will appear anything from three to thirty years later; during the intervening time the disease is latent. When it becomes active again it can attack any part of the body but particularly the central nervous system or the heart and blood vessels, and can result in death.

Congenital syphilis is passed on by an infected mother to her unborn child during the primary, secondary, and early tertiary stages of the disease. There is very little congenital syphilis in Britain because *every* pregnant woman is given a blood test early in pregnancy to see if she has contracted the disease. This makes it possible for it to be treated before the child has been damaged. Treatment is easy and reliable and usually consists of injections of penicillin. It is no more painful than injections for any other condition and those who try to frighten children with horror stories about the treatment given for these diseases have much to answer for. For those who are allergic to penicillin other drugs are available. It cannot be emphasized strongly enough that if treated early this disease can be cured completely and the cure is readily available, free of charge, confidential, and relatively painless. Even in the later stages it can be either cured or arrested.

Gonorrhoea is less serious but far more widespread. It has been described as a world-wide epidemic. Only the common cold and possibly measles are anything like so common. The gonococcus is a parasite on the human body and is quickly killed by exposure to air or weak antiseptics. It principally attacks the linings of the genito-urinary systems. The incubation period can be anything from two to ten days but is usually in the two to five day range. In some women it has been as long as thirty days. One of the most important facts about gonorrhoea is that over half the women who are infected have no symptoms and may for a long time be unaware that they have it. They are, however, still carriers of the disease and may themselves, at any time, develop complications. Those women who do develop symptoms will notice a vaginal discharge, possibly accompanied by irritation. A few get the infection in their urinary tract and develop urethritis and/or cystitis with frequent and painful urination.

Men usually develop a tingling of the penis followed by a thick greeny-yellow discharge. As the penis contains the urethra, infection inevitably means inflammation of the urethra. This urethritis causes frequent and very painful urination. Because of these symptoms men are much more likely to seek treatment than women. Often the first indication women have that they are infected is when their partner, or the clinic, informs them. Failure to obtain treatment may result in the infection passing upwards into the rest of the reproductive system and possibly causing sterility. It can also lead to arthritis and swollen joints.

As with syphilis the treatment is effective, virtually painless, free and confidential. Once again penicillin is the drug of choice, with substitutes available for those with allergies. Gonorrhoea is not passed on from the mother to the unborn child, but occasionally at birth the child's eyes may become infected, leading to blindness. This condition is fortunately rarely found in Britain today.

N.S.U. or non-specific urethritis is an inflammation of the urethra for which no specific cause can be found. This condition is increasing in Britain with about three times the speed of gonorrhoea. Part of this increase is, however, due to improved methods of diagnosis. Whilst it is thought that sexual intercourse is the usual mode of transmission, other methods of infection are possible. Until the cause of the condition is isolated it is impossible to be dogmatic. Symptoms usually occur from seven to twenty-eight days after sexual intercourse, but in some cases, especially in women, there may be no symptoms at all. Men get a discharge from the penis, a burning pain on passing water and a need to do so more frequently than usual. Sometimes the discharge is very slight and may not attract attention. It is often greatest first thing in the morning before passing urine. Women may get an inflammation of the cervix which is often not noticed. The complications of untreated N.S.U. are similar to those of gonorrhoea. As we have not isolated any specific cause, treatment can only be general, or empiric, and the results are not so satisfactory as with the other two diseases, relapses being frequent. It is usual to treat the partners of infected men even when the women have no symptoms. This is done to prevent re-infection. Tetracycline, streptomycin and the sulphonamides are among the drugs used to treat the disease.

Since the results of these diseases, when they are untreated, are so serious, and since it is so easy to cure them, everything possible must be done to make treatment as widespread as possible. Apart from the lack of publicity given to the availability of treatment, people are also prevented from seeking it because of shame or embarrassment. In the days when sex was considered as synonymous with sin, venereal disease was looked on as the wages of sin – a just punishment. Is it any wonder that people were afraid to seek treatment which was an admission of sin? We have got to get away from this and regard sexually transmitted diseases in the same way as we regard airborne diseases. They and their treatment must be brought out into the open. If enough time, effort, and money were put into the fight, these diseases could be beaten just as other diseases have been. So far there has been a certain amount of hesitancy because of the fear that if the threat of disease were removed then there would be nothing to curb sexual licence. This is a very negative viewpoint; people cannot be frightened into certain ways of behaviour, nor should they be. A positive outlook with positive teaching and a little more faith in human nature is what is needed.

One simple thing that would make it easier for people to seek treatment would be the integration of venereal disease clinics into genito-urinary outpatient departments of hospitals. These departments would deal with all disorders of the genito-urinary systems and no stigma would attach to anyone attending them.

Another difficulty is the lack of symptoms in women. Infectious but symptomless women provide a reservoir of infection that needs to be eliminated. This could be done by providing screening tests, perhaps on leaving school and at regular intervals afterwards. A great deal of contact tracing is already done by clinics who follow up as many as possible of the sexual partners of their clients. This is a difficult and time consuming but very worthwhile operation. Women would be well advised to make sure that any man with whom they have intercourse has their address. This will enable him to contact them if he develops symptoms. Men carry a great responsibility for informing any woman they suspect of being infected. If they cannot face doing it themselves then the clinic will do it for them.

So much for the spread, signs and symptoms, and cure; but prevention is better than cure and health education is concerned with prevention. There are preventive measures that can be taken. The first of these is chastity. If people do not indulge in sexual activity then they will not suffer from sexually transmitted diseases. Then there is sex that stops short of intercourse and this makes infection less likely. For those who have intercourse the best way of avoiding infection is to stick to one partner. It is casual sex relationships that are responsible for much of the spread of these diseases. Even here a great deal can be done to lessen the risks. The condom, properly used, gives a very high degree of protection, possibly as high as 95 per cent. After all, if it keeps the sperms in it will keep the germs in — or out as the case may be. Even women who are on the pill would be wise to insist on the use of a condom by any partner of whom they are not certain.

Above all, we must not use these diseases as a moral weapon. Let us by all means discuss sexual morality with our young people and try to see that they do not abuse their sexual gifts, but a disease is a condition that needs treatment, not a sermon. We must give up sermonizing if we really want to reduce the incidence of these ailments. It can be done if we bring them out into the open, and they are too serious to be used as moral whips.

In dealing with sexually transmitted diseases with any class, we must be honest. They need to know the dangers but we must, above all, avoid frightening them. Fear has a boomerang effect; if we make them afraid they will be loth to admit the possibility of infection in themselves and so they will not seek treatment. It is possible that fear may prevent some young people from indulging in pre-marital sex, but only at the price of making them afraid of sex altogether, which does not augur well for any later married happiness.

Further Reading

Catterall, R. D. *The Venereal Diseases.* (London: Evans, 1967.)
The Venereal Diseases. Offices of Health Economics, 1963.

20
Services Available

We live in a welfare state but many of the people who need its services most do not know what help is available or where to go to find out about it. Soon after leaving school our young people may find themselves involved with national insurance, unemployment, social security, or industrial injuries. Teaching them about these things is perhaps not strictly health education, but if their ignorance leads to worry, confusion, or deprivation, then their health will suffer. In many schools these things are dealt with in environmental studies, modern studies, or some other subject. We need to find out if it is being covered in our schools and, if not, we must fill in the gap. This can be done by giving small groups of pupils different services and benefits to investigate and pooling the knowledge gained. It would be useless trying to list benefits here as they change so rapidly. The local office of the Department of Health and Social Security will give up-to-date information, and so will the Department of Employment and Productivity.

The personal services, in particular the health services, are more our concern. When the National Health Service started in 1948 it was set up as a tripartite service. All hospitals and ancilliary hospital services were placed under the authority of Regional Hospital Boards, general practitioners and dentists were governed by Local Executive Councils and the Public Health Services were left with the Local Authorities. These three branches, though they might co-operate at times, were administratively quite separate. Although this has worked reasonably well the division has sometimes been irksome. Now they are to be integrated into one service under Area Health Boards. The whole of Britain will be covered by these boards, each of which will be responsible for all the health services in their area which were previously covered by the three bodies already named. This integration is timed to start in April 1974. Each board will be subdivided into districts in order to avoid becoming too remote from the people it serves.

It is difficult to say what effect this integration will have on the consumer. In the beginning we will probably hardly notice any differences. Our family doctor will still be a family doctor and the hospitals will remain havens for the sick. Ultimately the two should work more closely together for our benefit but so slowly that we shall probably hardly see it happening. The district nurses and midwives will not be any less welcome in our homes because they have been sent by the Area Health Board instead of the Local Authority. It does not matter who employs these people, it is what they do for us that counts. As health educators we need to know what services are available and where they can be found, and we must pass this knowledge on to the pupils.

The person most likely to be able to help us with this is the school health visitor. She is the general practitioner of the social services and part of her job is to call in the more specialized services when required. Because of this she must have a full knowledge of the services available in her area. The health visitor's job has been described as 'health education and social advice'. Much of her health education is individual in the homes of her clients, but she also undertakes group teaching and may well help with, or at least advise on, health education in schools. She has a wide knowledge of health, and teachers would find her an invaluable source of information. As the only social worker to visit normal homes regularly she has a unique knowledge of the community. Teachers worried about any of their pupils should contact the school health visitor who will be able to provide information about the home background and, if necessary, do home visits on behalf of the school.

The health visitor visits all babies from the day the midwife relinquishes responsibility until the child starts school. In the days when health visitors were responsible for geographical areas she then continued supervision of the child first in the primary and then in the secondary school. This gave her an intimate knowledge of the child from birth to sixteen years. In some areas this is still the case, but in more and more places she is moving from a geographical area to what is called general practitioner attachment. This means that one or more health visitors will work closely with a particular group of family doctors, visiting all the families registered with them as thought necessary. They still visit all the babies and most of the old people, but in addition they are able to help other people whose difficulties may be social or domestic rather than medical. There is often a district nurse working with the doctor and health visitor, and they complement each other. The doctor deals with the medical side, the district nurse with the nursing care, and the health visitor with the health education and social advice. The advantages of this team work far outweigh the loss, felt mainly by schools, of the knowledge of a particular area that the geographically based health visitor possessed. Still, every school and every pupil will be the responsibility of some health visitor, and whilst they might belong to different ones the health visitors will co-operate closely.

In the school the health visitor is responsible for the supervision of the children's health. In this she will work with the school doctor and may well be helped by a less highly-trained nurse. All children have a medical examination on entering and leaving school, and possibly one or two intermediate ones. When the doctor attends to do these routine inspections the health visitor will refer for a special examination any child giving cause for concern. She will also visit the home or take any other steps necessary to ensure that treatment recommended or advice given by the doctor is carried out.

Another of her responsibilities is the cleanliness of the pupils and she will either carry out herself, or delegate to her assistant, regular hygiene inspections. Routine tests for vision and hearing are also done by the health visitor and/or her assistant, unless the authority appoints specialists to do these tests. Immunization procedures are also arranged by her. These vary from area to area but will usually include the triple diptheria/whooping cough/tetanus immunization, tests for and possibly inoculation against tuberculosis and, for girls who have not had the disease, protection against German measles.

The health visitor is a State Registered Nurse with midwifery training who has undergone a year's course in preventive health, social work, and educational techniques. She could be an invaluable ally for any teacher of health.

Another important source of help is the social work department. Their range of activities is almost as wide as that of the health visitor but they are not usually called in until something has gone wrong. Here is a brief resumé of the services they offer.

Children

    Preventive case work with families who have problems
    Pre-school day centres (day nurseries)
    The registration and supervision of pre-school play-groups
    The adoption and fostering of children
    The provision of children's homes
    Reports and follow-ups for 'Children's Hearings'
      (formerly Juvenile Courts)

Physically handicapped

    The provision of Sheltered Workshops
    Domiciliary occupational therapy
    Aids and adaptations
    Arrangements of voluntary visiting
    Social clubs
    Hostels and Centres
    Holidays

Mentally subnormal

    Case work
    Day care
    Social Clubs
    Hostels
    Holidays

The elderly

Case work
Home Helps
Meals on Wheels
Old People's Homes
Sheltered housing
The arrangement of Voluntary Visiting

Social work

Reports and after-care work for courts
After-care work for prisons and borstals
Welfare services in prisons
Help for the homeless and 'down and outs'
The arrangement of the funerals of people without relatives

This wide list is by no means exhaustive and the services in your area would make a rewarding subject for study. There is also much scope here for involvement of the pupils in active work in the community. Nothing can more quickly help them to become responsible citizens than getting involved in some form of practical community service.

The Police and the Marriage Guidance Council are two other potential sources of help worth investigation. We must try to get young people to see the Police as helpers rather than pryers. The police forces themselves are usually very willing to help with this and often have good relations with schools. In quite a few areas members of the Marriage Guidance Council work with schools. They will usually be willing to take part in any health education programme.

Pupils also need to be aware of the services, essential to health, which are so much part of everyday life that we take them for granted. Without clean water and food, and hygienic disposal of sewage and refuse, we would soon be subject to various epidemics. These are matters that may well be dealt with by other disciplines, but we must not assume that this is so; it is our job to make sure and, if there is a gap, to fill it. Visits to waterworks and sewage plants are the best way to learn about the way public plumbing protects us. Regular refuse collection and sweeping of streets is essential, but do we do all we can to co-operate? What system does your school use to counteract the litter problem? Could it be improved?

Whose job is it to see that premises selling food are kept clean? If you buy some sausages that are unfit to eat, to whom do you take them? The answer in both cases is the Local Authority's Public Health Inspector. He has wide powers under the Food and Drugs and other Acts and will be able to give you a lot of useful information. Again it is possible that all this is being covered under 'Civics' or some other title. If so, welcome it, but if not, remember that these facilities are there to protect our health and that they all work more efficiently with the co-operation of an informed public.

Further Reading

Caplan, Gerald. *An Approach to Community Mental Health.* (London: Tavistock, 1969, chapters 6–8.)

Cullen, Margaret. *The Family and the Social Services.* (London: Heinemann Educational Books, 1973.)

Davies, J. B. Meredith. *Preventive Medicine, Community Health and Social Services.* (London: Bailière, 1966.)

Hughes, D. T. D. and Marshall, P. T. *Human Health, Biology and Hygiene.* (Cambridge University Press, 1970.)

21
Minor Ailments
and First Aid

We must, however, take some responsibility for our own health and we must learn to recognize and be able to deal with the more common minor ailments. As teachers we cannot avoid taking some degree of responsibility for the health of our pupils. In cases of sudden illness or accident we ought to be able to render very simple first aid. Let us look at some of the common minor ailments that we may meet in the classroom. Table 3 shows some common skin conditions:

Table 3   Skin Conditions

Condition	Cause	Symptoms	Treatment and/or Action
Scabies	A tiny mite which burrows under the superficial layers of the skin particularly between the fingers or any area where the skin is soft, e.g. flexures of elbows and knees, armpits, groins, and between the toes. It is highly contagious.	Redness and intense itching and irritation.	Refer to G.P. or School Health Service.
Ringworm	A fungus infection. May be caught from animals. Highly contagious. Usually on exposed areas of skin, but may affect feet, scalp, or rarely nails.	A raised red area often round in shape.	Refer to G.P. or School Health Service Sufferers are usually banned from swimming pools.
Verruca	Probably a virus infection. May be spread via communal bathmats, swimming pools, gymnasiums, changing rooms, etc.	A wart which occurs on the foot, often on the sole. It can be very painful.	Refer to G.P. or chiropodist or the School Health Service. Sufferers are usually banned from swimming pools.

Table 3 (contd.)

Condition	Cause	Symptoms	Treatment and/or Action
Athlete's foot	This is a fungus infection. May be spread via communal bathmats, swimming pool, gymnasium, changing rooms, etc.	A moist peeling of the skin between the toes. Causes itching and irritation. Walking becomes painful.	Refer to G.P. or School Health Service. Sufferers are usually banned from swimming pools.
Acne	An infection of the sebaceous glands which develop at puberty. Not infectious.	Blackheads, whiteheads, and pimples on the skin — often on face or back. They may irritate but their worst effects is the embarrassment they cause to adolescents.	Frequent washing with soap and water. A good diet. Fresh air and exercise. Severe cases should be referred to G.P. or School Health Service.

Two tiny insects can cause worry in the classroom out of all proportion to their size; they are fleas and head lice. Fleas are small, black, and incredibly active. They can jump easily and are very difficult to catch. Obviously they flourish and breed where there is a lack of cleanliness, but anyone, even teachers, will find that it is easier to be caught by them than to catch them. They bite the skin causing red raised areas and intense itching. Calomine lotion or an anti-histamine cream will ease the irritation but unless caught the flea will get hungry and start biting again. They are inclined to settle down to sleep (and digest their food!) in warm places such as the seams of garments and this, particularly if the garment is dark in colour, makes them hard to see. It is useful to undress and drop the clothes on to a white sheet or towel to make the flea visible. The head louse is causing concern because it is on the increase. Opponents of long hair are quick to blame it on this and, of course, they have a point, but we have all been a little too complacent about the head louse in the past few years. We assumed that it was defeated and relaxed our vigilance. Unlike fleas the head louse does *not* jump. It travels from head to head by means of a sedate and leisurely walk. Children frequently put their heads together or try on each other's hats, so that transfer from one child to another is easy. The louse is larger than the flea and takes on the colour of the hair of the host. It sucks blood from the scalp and causes itching. It lays its eggs in the snuggest and warmest places it can find, behind the ears and in the nape of the neck. Each egg, or nit, is fastened to a hair with a kind of cement. At first sight nits look rather like dandruff but, whereas dandruff can be flicked off with a finger, nits are extremely difficult to remove. There are preparations on the market, such as Prioderm and Esoderm, which will kill the lice and soften the cement, thus enabling the nits to be combed out. This must be done with a special fine-toothed comb and can be a laborious task, for if even one nit is left it may hatch out and start the cycle all over again. It is not only children who get head lice, parents and teachers are also at risk and in infected families it is necessary to treat all members who are affected.

Impetigo is a septic condition of the skin caused by infection of skin abrasions. It can be a complication of the bites of fleas, midges or head lice or pimples or any other skin injuries which have been scratched so much that the skin has been broken. Cases should be referred to the family doctor or the school clinic.

All teachers are troubled from time to time by children who 'smell'. This may be due to a simple lack of cleanliness but is commonly the result of bed-wetting. It is extremely difficult to prevent an habitual bed-wetter from smelling. We should never draw attention to this in front of the other children, but if the child is sensible and intelligent it might be worth trying to discuss it quietly. Since, however, it is usually beyond the child's control it is better to have a word with the health visitor who will visit the home.

We all need to be on the lookout for defects whether of vision, hearing, or anything else. Everyone has heard the story of the boy who was continually punished for looking out of the window instead of attending to what the teacher was saying and who was later found to have one defective ear. He was not looking out of the window but presenting the teacher with his good ear in a commendable effort at attention. Of course a lot of children do look out of the window and there are periodic hearing tests, but we should always have the possibility of a hearing defect at the back of our minds. The same applies to vision; if a child continually copies things from the board incorrectly the child may be dim or careless, but let us not foget that it may be due to our bad writing or to poor vision or even a combination of both. There are also children who lack dexterity and who cannot produce neat work however hard they try. To label such children as careless may be to do them a grave injustice. Any defects should be reported to the health visitor, who will take the necessary steps for investigation and/or treatment.

Most experienced teachers take accidents in their stride but newcomers can be worried by them. Whereas a little simple first-aid is essential, a more comprehensive knowledge would be ideal. Here are a few hints which will help, but all teachers would be well advised to take a course in first-aid.

Fits. The main treatment is to prevent injury by moving away any objects on which the child may hurt himself. Forcible restraint is useless. If possible remove any false teeth and put a folded handkerchief between the teeth to prevent the tongue being bitten, but never try to prise open the mouth for this or any other purpose.

Faints or any other unconsciousness where breathing is still functioning. Lie the child down in the semi-prone position (see Figure 8). Do not sit him on

Figure 8   The semi-prone position. (From *First Aid Manual,* St. Andrew's Ambulance Brigade.)

a chair with his head between his knees if he is feeling faint because if he does lose consciousness he could fall on his head. He should not have a drink until he is *fully* recovered.

Hysteria. Reassure him gently but firmly, and give him some occupation as soon as possible.

Nose bleeds. Put the patient with his head forward (preferably over a bowl or washbasin to catch drips) and get him to pinch firmly the soft part of his nose for ten minutes. If the bleeding does not stop seek medical aid.

Other bleeding. Apply pressure immediately over the wound. If there is a protruding bone or other foreign body in the wound build up a pad round it (see Figure 9). If it is a limb, elevate it.

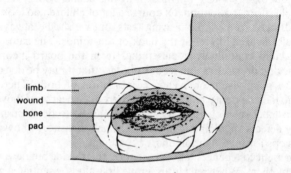

limb
wound
bone
pad

Figure 9

Burns. Reduce the heat as quickly as possible. The easiest way to do this is to put the affected area in cold water or put cold water on the area. Speed is vital, for so long as it remains hot, tissue is being damaged. Cover with a clean dry dressing.

Poisons. If the poison was not a corrosive (and if it was, the lips and mouth will be burned) make the patient vomit by tickling the back of his throat or giving him salt and water to drink. The exception to this is petroleum products, as they do little harm unless they are inhaled into the lungs and

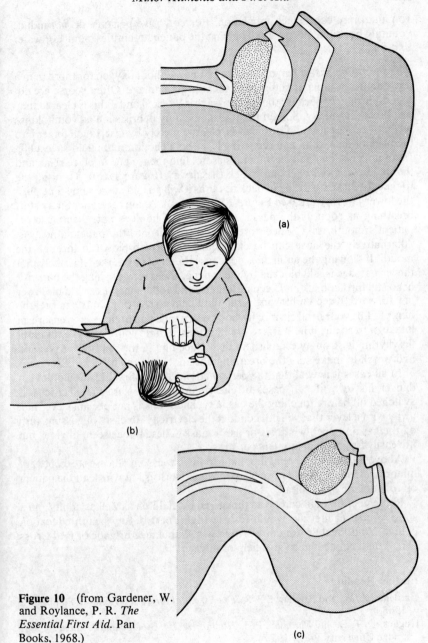

Figure 10 (from Gardener, W. and Roylance, P. R. *The Essential First Aid.* Pan Books, 1968.)

vomiting may cause such inhalation. For corrosive poisons, do *not* induce vomiting but dilute the poison by giving the patient quantities of milk or water to drink.

Non-breathing cases. Anyone whose brain is without oxygen for more than a few minutes will die or suffer permanent brain damage. Often people are not breathing merely because their air passage is blocked and if this is cleared they will breath normally. Sometimes it is blocked by debris such as vomit, loose teeth, or seaweed, and if so it can be cleared merely by inserting a finger into the back of the mouth and removing it – a small action that could save a life. In an unconscious person the muscles holding the tongue in place relax and the tongue can fall back and block the airway (Figure 10(a)). To bring the tongue forward, tip the head back as far as it will go and at the same time push the lower jaw forward (see Figure 10(b) and (c)). Again the patient may start breathing as soon as the passage is cleared. If he does not, then close the patient's mouth, take a deep breath and blow it into the patient's nostrils. Alternatively the nose can be closed and the breath blown in through the mouth. If blowing the air in does not cause the chest to rise then it is likely that the air passage is still blocked by the tongue. Clear it by pushing the patient's head still further back and keeping it there, and at the same time hold his lower jaw forward. Keep on blowing air in until help arrives or he starts to breathe himself. Lift your head clear of his body every time you breathe in to ensure an intake of fresh air. If he starts to breathe himself, time your breaths to his until his rhythm is strongly established, then place him in the semi-prone position and watch to make sure the breathing does not stop again.

In all cases it is vital that the person administering first aid should not endanger his own life. In cases of electrocution make sure the electricity is switched off before touching the casualty, and if this is not possible lever him away with a lever that will not conduct the electricity. In cases of gassing, turn off the gas and open windows or use a mask. These things seem obvious but are easily forgotten in moments of stress.

Above all, remember that first aid is only *first* aid; in all cases (except very minor ones, such as mild nose bleeds, whose cause is known) send the patient on to a doctor or hospital.

Remember first aid can be administered by children as well as adults and a short course in first aid would form a useful part of any health education course. Your local St John or St Andrew's Ambulance Brigade or Red Cross Unit would be pleased to give help or advice.

Further Reading

Gardener, A. W. and Roylance, P. R. *The Essential First Aid.* (London: Pan Books, 1968.)

Hughes, D. T. D. and Marshall, P. T. *Human Health, Biology and Hygiene.* (Cambridge University Press, 1970.)

22
Teeth and Feet

There is one facet of health education in schools that has probably had more time spent on it than any other with very doubtful results – it is dental health. The teeth of our children are a disgrace to us all and our own are little better. We know it is because we eat too many sweet, starchy, over-refined foods, yet once again knowledge is not enough. Our children are brought up to have a sweet tooth, to expect to be constantly chewing. Exhortations about finishing meals with apple or carrot fall on deaf ears. Attempts to get children to indulge in regular brushing meet with only moderate and usually temporary success. Some areas are resorting once more to public plumbing and are putting fluoride in their drinking water. There is no doubt about the fact that fluoride helps to prevent decay and most experts agree that it is harmless to health. But a few people claim that it does have some deleterious effect, others that the protection it offers is not permanent, and a much larger body of opinion objects to any chemical being forced on the population in this way. The fluoride controversy shows democracy at work. Is there fluoride in your water? If so, what effect do the dentists think it has had? If there is not, has it been suggested and is there any local opposition? If fluoride is added to the water and we no longer have to worry about our children's teeth, what effect might this have on sugar consumption? Would this matter?

Teeth may have had more than their share of time, but feet have been neglected with results that are not doubtful but disastrous. The state of our children's feet is as bad as the state of their teeth but we are less aware of it. It is a condition that worsens with age and many old people are house- or chairbound just because of the state of their feet. We all know how miserable aching feet can make us, and they affect our posture, which in turn displaces our abdominal organs and puts a strain on our spines. Bad feet put a strain on temper too and so adversely affect our social as well as our physical health. Our feet are bad because we wear the wrong kind of shoes and stockings or socks. Fife County chiropody service have recently undertaken a survey of children's feet. They examined the ffet, hosiery, and footwear of 5108 children aged either five, ten, or fifteen years old. Let me quote some of their findings:

'It is often taken for granted that in this day and age all children have their own shoes fitted at purchase. We found, however, that in the case of 5-year olds 1 in 13 children were not present at the purchase of their shoes and that at 10 years of age the number was 1 in 10. By 15 years of age, however, only 1 in 40 did not have a shoe fitting.'

Here are the figures they gave for ill-fitting shoes:

Table 4

Age	%Boys	%Girls
5	52.87	64.73
10	52.02	63.64
15	29.36	33.91

Over half the children of five years old had ill-fitting shoes and the position was not much better by ten years. We cannot put that down to fashion alone. Is it poor design or careless parents? Could it have anything to do with the high cost of shoes? What part does ignorance play? The pupils could do some research on their own and discuss the findings.

Hosiery can do as much damage as shoes. Stretch socks and tights only fit because they are stretched by the foot. If the foot has to stretch the sock then the sock must be pressing against the toe. Young toes are soft and easily deformed. Look at Fife's figures for ill-fitting hosiery:

Table 5

Age	%Boys	%Girls
5	25.56	38.12
10	26.05	34.21
15	6.56	55.08

The boys' socks fit better as they grow older but the opposite is true of the girls'. This is due largely to the wearing of one-size tights.

The Fife survey found many defects. Tables 6 and 7 show two examples:

Table 6   Hallux Valgus – a deformity of the big toe leading to a bunion

Age	%Boys	% Girls	%All
5	14.68	20.81	17.65
10	30.19	46.04	37.78
15	45.44	61.45	54.01

These figures speak for themselves and should convince us of the need for better fitting shoes. Since the trouble obviously starts before school age the parents of pre-school children need teaching. That is not our job except that

[1] Report in *Health and Social Service Journal,* 21 July 1973.

our pupils are tomorrow's parents. They also need to be educated about the importance of caring for their own feet. It is not always easy, however, because most shops only stock fashionable shoes and if the current fashion is bad for the feet then teenagers will have difficulty in getting the right type of shoes. (I myself have bitter experience of this.) There is, however, a ray of hope from Fife. As a result of the survey, plus the accompanying publicity and education, the shops selling fitted shoes reported increased sales and were

Table 7   Lesser toe anomalies

Age	%Boys	%Girls	All
5	45.17	58.23	49.07
10	50.22	51.42	50.80
15	57.54	56.73	56.04

increasing their stocks, whilst those shops that sold only fashion shoes were suffering recession of trade. The shops are there to sell shoes. In the end they will give us what we want if we tell them loud and clear and often. What do we want, what constitutes a well fitting shoe?

1. It must be the correct length for the foot.
2. It must be the correct width for the foot.
3. It must be the correct depth for the foot.
4. It must have a bar or lace or other fastening to hold the foot in place and prevent it slipping forward so that the toes are crushed.
5. It must have a low heel.

The colour and decoration can be left to the dictates of fashion but until the bones of the feet have finished growing they must not be crushed into shoes that do not fit properly. After the age of about eighteen years, minor, temporary lapses are of less importance.

Unfortunately the feet are still at risk during adolescence which is the time when the dictates of fashion are hardest to resist, but the consequences are so serious and long-lasting that we must do all in our power to help them to help their feet.

Further Reading

Davis, H. C. *et al. The Lecturer's Guide to the Mouth.* Gibbs Oral Hygiene Service, 1973.

Children's Footwear (Munro Report). (London: H.M.S.O., 1973.)

Pamphlets

Children's Shoes. SATRA, Satra House, Kettering, Northants.
Clarks' Foot Charts
Children's Shoes and Feet. Start-Rite Shoes, Norwich, Norfolk.
All About Shoes. Consumer Council, 3 Cornwall Terrace, London, N.W.1.
Jane and Miranda. British Medical Assoc., Tavistock Square, London, W.C.1.

23
Safety

Accidents are one of the major causes of death in our civilization and the more mechanized we become the more danger we will be in. The three most important categories are home, road, and industrial accidents. Every sane person is concerned about the rising death toll exacted by our roads, particularly as it is the young and healthy who are so often involved. When we read of ancient civilizations that used to tie their fairest maidens to rocks to be eaten by dragons we are superiorly interested in people who could indulge in such barbaric customs. Of course they did it from fear and we can sympathize with that emotion – we still feel it. Does it ever occur to us that we also feed our youths and maidens to dragons, metal dragons, on a bigger scale than ever before? And we do not have the excuse of fear, unless it is the fear of lower standards of living. Perhaps we are really afraid of losing our recently acquired comforts. How will future generations look back on our callous barbarism?

The terrible thing about our roads is that they get worse all the time and we all deplore this fact yet contribute to it. Perhaps the best hope we have is the oil shortage which may force sanity upon us. Until it does, schools must try to help their pupils to stay alive. Much is being done and more is planned. Five-year old school entrants are enrolled in Tufty Clubs (road safety clubs for young children organized by R.O.S.P.A.) and throughout their school life pupils are trained in, and reminded of, road safety. There are special patrolled crossings at the entrances to schools and our roads have a welter of devices aimed at making them less dangerous. The police and accident prevention councils are very active and spend a lot of time educating our children. They try to train them to cross the road and to cycle proficiently, and in some areas they even train them to drive. These people are specialists and can do the job far better than we can. It is an area of health education in which our job is to be aware of the size of the threat, to alert our pupils to it, to get them discussing the underlying philosophy, and to bring in the experts to help to train them for survival.

The Royal Society for the Prevention of Accidents will provide us with much useful material to aid our discussions. For younger pupils in secondary schools they have some very good work books which will help to make the pupils aware of dangers to themselves and others. At this stage too the police will often help to run training classes for cyclists, leading to proficiency tests.

Older pupils could look at car and road designs as well as at the human factors involved. A list of helpful books is given at the end of the chapter.

After walking along a busy road we enter the haven of home with a feeling of relief. The very word home conjures up feelings of security. We may feel safe at home, but we are not. Home accidents cause more suffering and death each year than do accidents on the road. There is far less awareness of the dangers involved, yet we have much more direct control over our homes than we have over our roads. If we are aware of the dangers we can avoid them. Some areas issue excellent handbooks on the subject. Aberdeen has a particularly good one[1] from which the following pages are taken:

Home Accidents and their Prevention

Before we look at the home room by room, it may be useful to indicate the common types of home accidents and how they can be prevented.

(1) *Falls*

Common causes include:

(a) Polished floors and small unanchored mats.
One of the slogans of the original Aberdeen Home Safety Campaign was –

'Polished floors and mats that slide –
That's the way that Grandma died.'

(b) The use of chairs and boxes as ladders and the use of rickety ladders and pairs of steps (see Figure 11).

(c) Objects left on stairs and in other places where they can cause people to trip.

(d) Insufficient lighting on stairs and in passages. Another Aberdeen slogan was –

'Toys and stairs and dismal lighting
Cause more broken bones than fighting.'

(e) Grease spilt on floor and not immediately removed.

(f) Loose stair carpets or worn covering on stairs.

(g) Trailing electric flexes.

(h) Down-at-heel slippers and trailing shoe laces.

(i) Unbarred windows in a room where a toddler plays.

(j) Absence of gate at top and bottom of stairs.

(2) *Cuts*

(a) Leaving knives, scissors, needles and razor blades within reach of young children.

[1] *Home and Road Safety* City of Aberdeen Health Committee.

Figure 11

  (b) Improper use of such implements by children who have been in-adequately taught about how to handle them.

  (c) Over-hurried use of these implements by adults, especially those who are tired or emotionally disturbed.

  (d) Giving babies or young children sharp-edged or pointed toys.

(3) *Burns and Scalds*

  (a) Absence of fireguards, or use of fireguards which are insecurely fixed. For all fires – coal, gas or electric – efficient guards are essential where there are children or old people.

  (b) Leaving the handles of cooking utensils and the spouts of kettles projecting outwards from the stove, so that a young child can reach up and pull the contents down on himself.

  (c) Use of celluloid toys which are highly flammable.

  (d) Use of tablecloth with edge hanging down (instead of turned under or held by clips), so that a toddler can pull hot tea over himself.

  (e) Leaving the electric iron switched on if called away while ironing.

(f) Carelessness with cigarette ends.
(g) Airing clothes on a fireguard close to a fire, or airing clothes by hanging them from a mantelpiece.
(h) Failing to place matches out of reach of young children, or failing to train slightly older children as to the proper use of matches.
(i) Placing baby in a bath without testing that the water is not too hot.
(j) Hanging mirrors over unguarded fires (see Figure 12).

(4) *Poisoning*

Points to note are –
(a) Keep all poisonous substances well out of reach of children.
(b) Remember that an ordinary medicine taken by adults may poison a child: put the aspirin bottle and the iron pills carefully away after use.
(c) Household cleaning materials are also poisonous to children.
(d) Keep your medicine cupboard locked.
(e) Never take medicines in the dark; always follow the instructions on the bottle, and measure the dose – don't just guess it.

Figure 12

(5) *Suffocation*

(a) Baby should have his own bed and should never sleep with his parents.

(b) No pillow at all is best for baby; and a soft pillow is really dangerous.

(c) If baby is bottle-fed hold him in the natural position as if for breast-feeding. Never leave him to feed alone from a propped-up bottle.

(d) Help him to bring up wind afterwards by holding him carefully over your shoulder or arm, and rubbing his back gently but firmly from the bottom to the top.

(e) If he wears a plastic bib, it should be firmly secured in the front, or else it may blow over his face and cause suffocation. Remove the bib before putting baby down to sleep.

(f) If you are going to leave him alone in his pram, fit a net over the top – to prevent animals from jumping into the pram and to keep out flying insects.

(6) *Swallowing of Substances*

It is important that babies and toddlers are given only safe toys, and that buttons etc., are securely fixed. Remember, incidentally, that while angora wool looks attractive, it is dangerous for babies: they tend to pull at the fluffy bits and to try to eat the wool.

(7) *Electrical Mishaps*

These are rather common but can be serious. Points to note include –

(a) In houses with children the shutter type of plug point is advised.

(b) Repairs should be carried out only by a qualified electrician.

(c) Never take portable electrical appliances into the bathroom.

(d) Never touch a metal switch with wet hands.

(e) Avoid using long flexes, especially twisted over nails and run under carpets.

(f) At night see that all electrical appliances not in use (e.g. wireless and television sets and portable fires) are switched off and disconnected from the mains.

(g) See that fuses are mended only with fuse wire of the correct rating.

(h) Do not connect too many electrical appliances to the same point, and never connect heating appliances to lighting points. These practices cause over-heating of circuits.

(i) Disconnect electric fires, washing machines, etc., when not in use; it is by no means unknown for a child to cause an accident by starting up an electric wringer.

(8) *Gas Mishaps*

These are uncommon but serious. Safety taps are desirable, so that children cannot turn them on. Care should be taken to ensure that all gas taps are properly turned off, and that gas burners when turned low cannot be blown out. Needless to say a gas leak, however small, should never be traced by a naked light.

(9) *Mishaps with Oil Heaters*

Portable oil heaters, like other portable heaters, can cause fires. Important points are –

(a) Use the heater only in an adequately ventilated room.
(b) See that it is level and unlikely to be knocked over.
(c) See that it is well away from draughts.
(d) See that it is well away from combustible materials.
(e) Do not lift or move the heater while it is alight.
(f) Use paraffin only.
(g) Store the paraffin in closed metal containers, if possible in an out-building.
(h) Heaters should not be filled while alight. Do not overfill.
(i) Never use a damaged heater.
(j) In the event of fire involving a paraffin heater do *not* use water: it only spreads the flame. Smother the fire with a rug or other suitable heavy material, or with a wet sack.

Your Dangerous Kitchen (see Figure 13)

1. Containers of poisonous household substances (bleach, disinfectant, etc.)

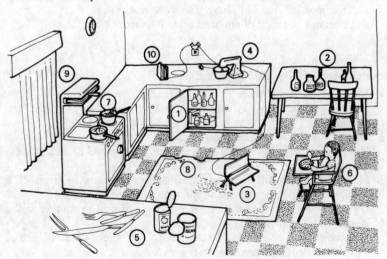

Figure 13 Your dangerous kitchen.

Should be out of a child's reach, locked up if possible. And should be in their correctly labelled bottles.
2. Jars and bottles that break to make jagged edges.
Should be out of a child's reach. Never give a child an empty bottle or jar to play with.
3. Unguarded electric fire and dangerous flex to fall over.
If you must have the fire have it fitted with a guard and tuck the flex behind furniture out of the way.
4. Heavy objects that a child can pull on to itself.
These should be well in from the table edge out of reach of a child's arm.
5. Cutlery and open tins that can cause cuts.
Keep cutlery shut away when not in use and throw all opened and empty tins away at once.
6. Child's chair without safety straps.
A child can easily fall out as it climbs around – straps are cheap to buy and easy to fit.
7. Saucepans full of scalding liquids, with handles overhanging the cooker edge.
Turn saucepan handles inwards and if possible fix a rail around the edge of the stove.
8. Frayed mat edge on the floor to trip over.
Sew up frayed edges or fit with a strip of material. Preferably do away with mats on a kitchen floor.
9. Curtain dangerously near the gas flames on the stove.
Tie curtains neatly back out of reach of the gas flames.
10. Electric iron left out and plugged in when not in use.
Put iron out of reach of children when finished with.

Your Dangerous Living Room (see Figure 14)
1. Unguarded open coal fire.
Guards are cheap to buy, easy to fit and absolutely safe varieties are obtainable.
2. Dangerous flex to fall over and unguarded electric fire.
Have the fire checked by an electrician. Have a guard fitted and tuck the flex behind furniture out of the way.
3. Mirror above the fireplace – a most dangerous place. A dress of a woman or child looking into the mirror could easily catch fire.
Guard the fire and move the mirror to a safer position on another wall.
4. Teapot that a child could pull on to itself.
This should be well in from the table edge out of reach of a child's arm.
5. Frayed mat edge on the floor to trip over.
Sew up frayed edges or fit with a strip of material.

6. Child's toys left in dangerous places on the floor.
   Clear all toys away after use, they could easily cause a nasty fall, especially to older folk.
7. Curtains dangerously near the electric fire – in draught from the window.
   Move the fire from the curtains and, in any case, guard the fire!
8. Too highly polished floor and slip mat at door entrance.
   Though floors should be clean, never polish so highly that they are dangerous and never polish under mats.
9. Fraying picture cord badly mended.
   Pictures like these are heavy and a fall could have serious results. Always fit new cords when needed – do not merely patch up.
10.. Cigarette smouldering on table edge.
   Provide ash trays – even if you don't smoke, your friends may do. Always stub out your cigarette.

Figure 14   Your dangerous living room.

Your Dangerous Bedroom (see Figure 15)

1. Unguarded electric fires are dangerous.
   Guards are cheap to buy, easy to fit and safe. Always use one. In any case do not place near bedding.
2. Dangerous flex to fall over.
   Tuck flexes behind furniture out of the way or fit a new plug point closer to the fire's usual position.

3. Frayed carpet on the floor to trip over.
   Sew up frayed edges or fit with a strip of material.
4. Cigarettes – for smoking in bed.
   Never smoke in bed – it is a dangerous habit as you could fall asleep and set yourself alight!
5. Drugs and cleaners left out on the dressing table.
   Such items can be dangerous and should be locked away in a cupboard out of the children's reach.
6. Bedclothes draped too close to the electric fire.
   A small point perhaps but such clothes could soon begin to scorch and burst into flame!

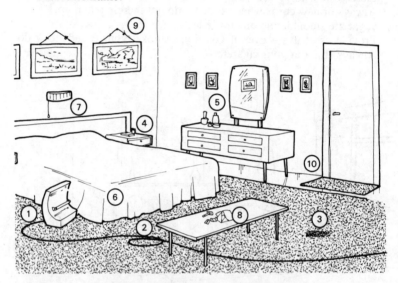

Figure 15   Your dangerous bedroom.

7. Badly frayed flex to electric light and behind bed.
   Such flexes can cause fuses or shocks. Check flexes every so often and get worn ones replaced by an electrician.
8. Razor and blades left out after use.
   Put away directly after use in a cupboard or case out of the children's reach.
9. Fraying picture cord badly mended.
   This picture is heavy and would seriously injure one if it fell. Always fit new cords when needed – do not merely patch up.
10. Floor too highly polished and slip mat at door entrances.
    Floors should be clean but not like skating rinks – never polish under mats.

Your Dangerous Bathroom (see Figure 16)

1. Dangerous drugs and cleansers in a low cabinet and on window ledge.
   Keep such items in a locked cupboard well out of a child's reach (and
   don't hang the key within reach of a child either).
2. Unguarded electric fire close to bath.
   This could fall into the bath or could be touched by a wet hand. If an
   electric fire must be used (and must it?) it should be fixed out of reach
   and guarded.
3. Bar of soap left on floor.
   Soap is slippery and a nasty fall could be caused. All soap in the proper
   receptacle please.
4. Polythene bags within easy reach of a child. Temptation to children
   and these bags can be very dangerous indeed if misused.
   Hang well out of reach or find an alternative for holding flannels, etc.

Figure 16   Your dangerous bathroom.

5. Frayed mat on the floor to trip over.
   Sew up frayed edges or fit with a strip of material. Non-slip rubber
   mats are far better.
6. Razor and razor blades left out after use.
   Put away directly after use in a cupboard or case.
7. Your first aid box should be fully equipped.
   Replace items when used up so that you always have anything you
   need.

8. Clothes drying too near unguarded fire and cord in dangerous position.
   If clothes must be dried in the bathroom fit a proper portable dryer that can be pulled up out of reach.
9. Tap placed so that children could swivel boiling water over their hands.
   Water heater's arm should be out of reach of children even if this means fixing it.
10. Celluloid toys (for children's bathtime) – most unsafe.
    Use plastic or rubber toys at all times.

Your Dangerous Garden (see Figure 17)

1. Uncovered water butt with coal bin adjacent. Children will climb on things and could easily fall into the butt and even a butt full of water will drown a child.
   Put a cover of wood or firm wire mesh over the butt.
2. Tools left out on the path to fall over.
   Tools should be put back in the shed after use always.
3. Tins of insecticide and poison left out.
   These should be out of a child's reach and locked up.
4. A pond has enough water to drown a toddler.
   Should be covered by wire mesh or have a fence fixed close around.

Figure 17 Your dangerous garden.

5. Boughs overhanging the greenhouse.
   Children climb trees and a fall from the bough into the greenhouse might be fatal. For safety's sake top boughs that overhang greenhouses or similar buildings.
6. Glass embedded in a wall may have stopped Victorian burglars. Today it is out of place and does more harm than good. When lopping the tree a fall could land you on top of this jagged glass with serious results.
7. Deckchair canvas can rot.
   It should be checked each spring after winter disuse. Dampness can weaken the canvas, with bad results to elderly folk who could fall through.
8. Bonfires can spread.
   This one (Figure 17) is far too close to the shed (with its can of petrol) and to the hedge. It should be well away from both.
9. These steps should never be used with a rung missing.
   Some day dad will forget and (nearly) break his neck.
   Mend at once.
10. The road gate is wide open.
    Always keep it shut (or see that others shut it) to stop toddlers straying on to the road.

Your Dangerous Hall

Lighting by day? People may enter hurriedly from brightly lit street or garden.
Lighting during darkness? Is that lampshade as efficient as it is decorative? Do shadows hide a roughed-up mat or a child's toy?
Mats? Are they the non-slip variety?
Forgotten toys, balls, dusters, brushes?

Some General Points

Here are a few extra points –

1. In a room where children normally play, have no inessential furniture or equipment.
2. Before you go to bed ask yourself – 'Is everything in its normal place? Is nothing so positioned that I might knock into it if I had to rise during the night?'
3. When did you last have your electrical equipment checked?
4. For jobs out of reach (like changing a high electric bulb) use a pair of steps or a stout kitchen chair.
5. Is your stair carpet securely fixed, with rods or clips functioning properly?
6. Is the stair free from obstructions? And is it properly lit?

7. For children and old people hot bottles should have covers, to reduce the possibility of burns.
8. For old people a rubber mat in the bath may prevent slipping and a fixed handrail beside the bath is useful.

A B C of FIRE PREVENTION

Airing clothes should not be left in front of an unguarded open fire.
Burning coal should never be carried from one fire to start another.
Chimneys should be swept regularly.
Draperies and curtains must be kept clear of portable fires.
Electrical repairs should be carried out by experts.
Flannelette and winceyette are highly flammable.
Gas fires, like coal and electric fires, need guards.
Hot ashes should never be placed in a wooden container.
Inflammable liquids, like paraffin, should be kept in a cool place, far from a fire.
Junior will move the fireguard unless it is fixed.
Kettles and saucepans may overbalance if placed on a fire.
Lighters are attractive to toddlers.
Matches should be out of reach of young children.
Never 'draw' the fire with a sheet of newspaper.
Overfilling of paraffin stoves is dangerous.
Portable stoves and fires should be so placed that they are not easily knocked over.
Quality is important in electrical fittings.
Red-hot pokers are to be avoided.
Smoking in bed is dangerous.
Tobacco ash and cigarette ends should go into ashtrays.
Unguarded fires are killers.
Veterans and toddlers are the people at greatest risk.
Wax candles need to be fixed securely in candlesticks.
X is the unknown risk not mentioned in this list: can you find it?
Youngsters should be taught to use matches correctly.
Zanies take needless risks while wise people avoid them.

THE HUMAN ELEMENT

(a) *Keeping Baby Safe*

A helpless but precious new life begins in a busy, bustling world. That life must be preserved by worthy parents as far as humanly possible. A few simple hints listed below should be observed and followed. Many babies have been injured and many little lives lost through neglect.

1. Never use a soft pillow – the baby might suffocate. No pillow at all is best.
2. Let baby sleep in his own bed or cot. He is too tiny and easily hurt to share his parents' bed. His cot rails should not be more than three inches apart so that his head cannot get between them.
3. Whilst baby is being fed hold and support him properly in order that no harm can come to him.
4. Don't leave baby alone with his bottle – he may choke.
5. Put cold water in his bath before hot, and test the bath with your elbow before using. Do not test with finger only.
6. Do not leave articles lying around within reach which he may swallow.
7. Protect his pram to stop cats and dogs jumping on the baby and injuring him.

(b) *The Inquisitive Toddler*

More than a third of all home accidents involve children of pre-school age. Here are some points to note –

1. *FIRES ARE INTRIGUING* (see Figure 18)
    Solution: All fires (coal, gas or electric) must be guarded in the presence of children under seven.

2. *OPEN WINDOW*
    Solution: Secure all windows in reach of child or fix vertical bars closely together so that the child cannot fall out or get his head fixed in them.

Figure 18

Figure 19

Figure 20

3. *STEAM IS FASCINATING* (see Figure 19)

   Solution: Place all vessels holding hot liquid well out of reach. Also turn saucepan handles inwards.

4. *PEEP·A·BOO is a Game. BUT NOT WITH TABLECLOTHS*

   Solution: Fold the cloth over so that it is out of harm's way.

5. *PYJAMAS* are in general safer for toddlers than *NIGHTGOWNS*.

6. *SCISSORS AND MATCHES*

   Solution: Keep them out of reach.

7. *THE STAIRS* (see Figure 20)

   Solution: Remember gates at top and bottom, and discourage play on stairs and in kitchen.

DO YOU REALIZE THAT ...

(c) There are some places in the home where the toddler can be burned or scalded other than the most obvious ones of the open fire and the kettle of water.

YOU MUST THEREFORE THINK FOR YOUR CHILD AND ACT AS ITS GUARDIAN. THE RESPONSIBILITY IS YOURS AND CANNOT BE PLACED UPON THE SHOULDERS OF ANOTHER.

THE HUMAN ELEMENT

(d) *The Tired Housewife*

Three points should be remembered –

1. Familiarity breeds carelessness:
   Accidents occur, not in new tasks, but in familiar daily tasks; not with new appliances, but with old appliances wrongly handled.
2. Carelessness causes accidents.
   Order, tidiness and method all help to reduce accidents.
3. Tiredness predisposes to accidents.
   Special care should be taken at the end of periods of maximum household activity.

(e) *Old People*

Falls are particularly common in the elderly, and old bones are easily broken. Here are some points –

1. Good lighting is especially important where eyesight is defective.
2. Old people are sometimes forgetful – why not paint the odd step on the stair or lobby white, so that it will be noticed? Keep floors free from obstructions.
3. Badly fitting slippers and trailing shoe-laces are frequent causes of falls in old people.
4. An old person needs a fireguard as much as does a child (see Figure 21).
5. If you cannot persuade your elderly relative to make her home less dangerous, why not enlist the help of the old person's health visitor?'

Figure 21

The home economics department of the school may well be able to give practical demonstration of home hazards, and the school health visitor will also provide help and advice.

Soon after leaving school many of our pupils will be working in industry.

The number of people killed at work or dying of diseases contracted at work is over 2000 annually. 70 000 workers are injured by cutting instruments, there are 19 563 fractures, 16 000 burns, 14 455 lacerations, 13 000 falls from ladders and scaffolding, 1799 cases of concussion, 14 000 cases of a foreign body in the eye, 1096 dislocations, 1489 amputations, 7920 crushings and 34 000 people who are injured just falling over at work. In all no less than 796 000 workers are injured each year in Britain[2]. In educating our pupils we cannot ignore the fact that about a quarter of their life for fifty years or so will be spent at work. We educate them so that they will be able to do a job; can we not go a bit further and try to equip them to stay alive and healthy whilst they are doing it? Industrial health and safety does not usually loom very large on a school curriculum and it is not a subject many feel competent to handle. Certainly we would need expert help. Some of this will be found within the school in the teachers in the technical departments. They already teach safety so far as their own craft is concerned and many would be willing to look at it in a wider context. Then there is the physical education specialist who can, and often does, teach such things as how to lift heavy weights without injury. Outside school we need to enlist the support of local industry. Many of the larger concerns have industrial safety officers who may be willing to help with training in schools. Anything we can do, however small, that will help to cut the terrible accident figures I have quoted, will be worthwhile.

Further Reading

Department of Employment and Productivity Series on Safety Health and Welfare in Industry. H.M.S.O.

Hughes, D. T. D. and Marshall, P. T. *Human Health, Biology and Hygiene.* (Cambridge University Press, 1970.)

Hunt, John H. *Accident Prevention and Life Saving.* (Livingstone, 1965.)

Nader, R. *Unsafe at Any Speed.* (New York: Grossman, 1965.)

Road Craft. (London: H.M.S.O., 1968.)

Skillman, T. S. *Road Safety.* (London: Re-appraisal Society, 1965.)

[2] Figures taken from *British Clinical Journal* vol 1, no. 2, July 1973.

24
Pollution and Population

Pollution is a word that has probably been used more in the last five years than it has in the preceding five hundred years. It is impossible for us to read, or watch television programmes, about current events without meeting the word. What does it mean and has it anything to do with health? It means the corruption, if not destruction, of our environment, and as we depend on our environment for survival it is of vital concern to our health.

Pollution takes many forms, from the destruction of the Vietnamese countryside with napalm and defoliants to toffee papers in our city streets. Man has always exploited and polluted the world, but it is only recently that the scale of pollution has become so great that it threatens our very existence. There are two main causes for this. The first, and most important, is the vast increase in the world population. If the world population doubles then, without any increase in individual consumption, the amount of the world's resources needed to maintain that population is also doubled. So is the amount of waste material produced and much of this waste material is harmful to our environment.

The second cause is our consumer society, which encourages us to want more of more kinds of things than ever before. Many of these things have what we call built-in obsolescence. Our forebears built things to last; we build things to discard and replace with an ever increasing frequency. Cheapness and labour-saving are more important than anything else. But we think of cheapness only in terms of money, not of world resources. A good example of this is paper pants. They are cheap to buy and completely expendable. Having been worn once they are discarded. They save us the effort of washing and ironing. These qualities make them seem an ideal product for modern man, or woman. If, however, we look at the situation more closely the picture is less rosy. Paper is still made from wood and our despoliation has already made wood a scarce product. Unless we husband our supplies there will soon be a real shortage. Are paper pants the best use to which we can put this precious commodity? Once worn these pants are discarded and immediately they add to our litter problem. If every member of an average household of four people used a new pair of paper pants every day that would mean twenty-eight pairs of paper pants to be added to the refuse of every household every week. How many per week for a big city? Even the fact that they do not need washing can add to our troubles. Already some people have more leisure than they know what to do with. One of the doubtful 'benefits' of labour-saving devices can be boredom. Fortunately the use of paper pants is not yet widespread and they have disadvantages that might limit their popularity. A friend of mine once wore them whilst sailing in mixed company. The weather was rough, he got soaked, the pants disintegrated and appeared piecemeal from the bottom of his trousers. But we all make use of tissues and paper handkerchiefs and all that has been said about paper pants applies equally to them. Perhaps your class could work out the cost, in resources and pollution, not money, of many of our small modern conveniences such as tissues, packaging, plastic containers, foil, synthetic sponges and foam rubber cushions, mattresses, etc.

All these arguments, of course, apply with even greater force to big things such as cars, freezers, refrigerators, and cookers. In the veteran car rally we see models over seventy years old; they were built to last. How many of our modern cars will survive to run in rallies which might be held seventy years from now? After ten or fifteen years they are ready for the scrap heap. The tragedy is that although the car is made from metals which are becoming more and more scarce, no one will take the trouble to recycle the metal; it is just left to rust and to disfigure the countryside. We are told that it would cost too much, in terms of money, but surely it is time we stopped thinking in terms of something so artificial as money and started to reckon the cost in terms of raw materials. Can we afford to waste precious metal or allow our countryside to be ruined by rusting wrecks? Unemployment, with all its resulting evils of boredom, frustration, and a feeling of uselessness, looms continually on the horizon; a lot of very useful, even vital work could be provided by recycling the materials from our disused cars, radios, television sets, refrigerators, and other discarded household gadgets.

We are despoiling our countryside in many ways too. There is the urban sprawl which is turning vast stretches of our countryside into suburbs and motorways. All motorists appreciate good roads and all human beings need homes in which to live. But we need other things as well and we cover our green land with concrete at our peril.

'I am alluding to the rise in the level of carbon dioxide in the atmosphere, a rise co-incident with that of the consumption of fossil fuels – coals and oil. Of course, if there were double the amount of carbon dioxide in the air that there is, it would not interfere with out health in any way as far as we know. But in the biosphere as a whole carbon dioxide is powerful stuff. There is a carbon dioxide cycle which naturally keeps levels right. It is a system of great age and stability which we are now taxing with the immense amounts of carbon dioxide we are adding from the fuel we burn. Vegetation is a great buffer: the forested wilderness removes a great deal of the carbon dioxide by the photosynthetic activity of the leaves, turns it into wood, and so sequesters it, giving out oxygen in exchange. It happens that a higher carbon dioxide content of the air creates a greenhouse effect, favouring tree growth, which locks up the carbon again until a lower level is restored. But unfortunately we are cutting the virgin wilderness all the time and reducing tree cover in so many places.

The oceans also soak up carbon dioxide and lock up carbon in the deeps. But the increasing concentration of carbon dioxide in the air leads to a gradual warming of the oceans so that they can hold less. The activities of industrial and technological man in our day are adding carbon dioxide and also injuring the capacity of the biosphere to redress the balance. All combustion is burning carbon or its compounds in oxygen – a single jet plane crossing the Atlantic uses thirty-five tons of it – and we are reducing the kind of plant cover which would help lock up the carbon dioxide produced. . . . The warming oceans would alter considerably the distribution of the marine fauna. This has happened already in this country in the warming of the Atlantic Ocean and has interfered with existing fisheries. Of course, through time fisheries adapt to new conditions, but there is another adaptation that would be much harder. The warming oceans and atmosphere would mean a recession of the polar ice caps. The Greenland ice is 9000 feet thick, so if that were to melt, with an equivalent melting of the Antarctic ice, the levels of the oceans would rise considerably. Our ports would go under quite literally, and with them vast tracts of fertile soil. What happens to the swarming human population? I suppose they move upwards and back, very slowly, of course, but surely. And what then?'[1]

Already more than two thirds of the earth's surface is covered by ocean and for every square mile of the remaining third there are forty people 'living and partly living'.[2] We must prevent further encroachment of the ocean and this means that we must stop the process which is turning our green oxygen-producing, carbon dioxide-absorbing land into concrete deserts. At the same time we must not only stabilize but decrease the world's population. People need food, fuel, homes, and space, but they also need oxygen. We cannot have our cake and eat it and the size of the world's cake is finite. It will only sustain a limited number of people. We may not know the actual number of human beings the earth is capable of maintaining, but we do know that we are well on the way to exceeding it. Population control we must have and we must have it quickly.

Our countryside is being exploited as never before in an effort to feed our growing numbers, and to increase the growers' profits. Jonathan Swift tells us that 'whoever could make two ears of corn or two blades of grass to grow upon a spot of ground where only one grew before, would deserve better of mankind, and do more essential service to his country than the whole race of politicians put together'[3], but leaving aside our opinion of politicians, this is no

[1] Darling, Sir Frank Fraser. *Wilderness and Plenty,* Ballantine, p. 61, 1969.
[2] Eliot, T. S. *Murder in the Cathedral.*
[3] *Gulliver's Travels* by Jonathan Swift.

longer necessarily true. It all depends on how he does it. If it is achieved by the unwise use of insecticides and chemical fertilizers then he may well have disturbed the delicate but essential balance of nature and his victory will be short-lived. He will also have helped to pollute our land, streams, and rivers. Fish, insect, animal, and bird life will suffer and, since man is an integral part of it all, he too will suffer.

The land is being raped by the advancing towns, poisoned by chemicals, and exhausted by too intensive farming. Hedges which absorb carbon dioxide, give out oxygen, and provide shelter for wild-life are being uprooted to make way for mechanical monsters which burn up fuel, descrate the land, and pollute the atmosphere. Our rivers and streams are foul with chemicals and human sewage and many of them can no longer maintain fish. Even the sea has, with some justification, been called 'dilute shit'. If all this had been done to feed the hungry two-thirds of the world's population it would have been short-lived and unwise, but as it has been done for profit and to garnish the tables of the already over-fed, then it is either insane or criminal. When we read of wheat or butter being destroyed because the price is not right, whilst elsewhere people die from lack of food, then we realize that if mankind is to survive he will have to do some drastic rethinking. Original thinking comes more easily in youth and anyway our young people have more (of their lives) to lose. The future is in their hands, but temporarily they are in ours. It is a tremendous responsibility but a wonderful opportunity. We must make them aware of what is happening to the world in which they are living.

Contact with the local conservation societies could be very fruitful. An investigation into the pollution problems of the area would be a useful way of getting them interested and could lead on to national and world problems. Even a survey of the school playground and an onslaught on school litter could make a useful beginning. Noise must not be forgotten and the study of this can also begin in the school or youth club. School playgrounds, transistor radios, and juke boxes can between them add considerably to the noise level of the area. Add to this the traffic on the road and in the sky and the picture becomes alarming. Too much noise damages the ear and the temper. There will probably be a local branch of the Noise Abatement Society who will help.

But it all boils down to people. The more people there are the more houses, cars, refrigerators, aeroplanes, fuel, and food they need, and the more waste materials they have to dispose of. People also need space. Like rats we get aggressive if we are overcrowded. Living as we do on a small overcrowded island, eating refined foods grown with chemical fertilizers, breathing polluted air, taking far too little physical exercise, having continually to strive to keep up with the Joneses, it is no wonder that we are far from healthy. We hear a lot about tension and stress, most of us suffer from them and with good reason. But let us not imagine that there is anything new about stress. In the good old days the fortunate few lived a leisurely, relatively stress-free life, but the great majority of our forebears had a much harder life than we now have. There is a great deal of stress involved in not knowing where your next meal is coming from, and whilst we lack physical exercise they usually had far too much of it. Looking back nostalgically will get us nowhere. Our present health is in our own hands, which takes us back to the first three chapters of this book. Our future lives and the life of the whole world are also in our hands. If we go on as we are there will be no future. It is no use educating our pupils unless we educate them about the realities of the world in which they live. That world is in danger, the human race is in danger, and our urgent task is to alert them to that danger whilst there may still be time to avert it.

Further Reading

Air Pollution and Health. A Report of the Royal College of Physicians, 1970.
Darling, Sir Frank Fraser. *Wilderness and Plenty.* (London: Ballantine, 1969.)
Dubros, R. and Ward, B. *Only One World.* (London: Pelican, 1972.)
Ehrlich, Dr Paul R. *The Population Bomb.* (Ballantine, 1971.)
Howe, G. Melvyn. *Man, Environment and Disease in Britain.* (Newton Abbot: David and Charles, 1972.)
Tolstoy, Ivan. *The Pulse of a Planet.* (Signet, 1971.)

25
Fitting it into the Curriculum

All education but particularly health education is aimed at changing opinions and thinking habits in order to change behaviour, and it is a permanent change in behaviour that we want. Such a long-term aim requires a carefully thought out, well-presented programme spread out over the pupil's whole school life. What is the best method of achieving this? It will obviously not be by short bursts of activity undertaken in response to crisis situations, or by isolated visits from outside specialists. The specialists can make a valuable contribution but only as part of a continuing course. Emotive subjects such as drugs or sex should never be highlighted or treated in isolation, for this might encourage the experimentation that so many people dread. Such subjects should always be part of a comprehensive syllabus. It is, after all, a short and unemotional step from the effect of food on the body to the effect of drugs on the body.

It is easy to say what we should not do, but it is not very helpful. Health education requires time, it must have a balanced and integrated programme, and above all it needs committed teachers. There are innumerable ways of fitting health education into the school curriculum but most of them can be included under one of the following three headings:

1. Farming it Out

Theoretically everyone can and should be involved in health education. It could impregnate the whole of the curriculum without ever appearing on the time-table. Every subject discipline has a contribution to make. Here are a few indications of ways in which the various subjects could contribute, but it is by no means an exhaustive list.

(a) *Biology, anatomy and physiology* – a base on which to build, e.g. when the respiratory system is taught, the effects of smoking and pollution on that system could be included.
(b) *Physical education*. The benefits of exercise and the joys of a healthy body.

(c) *Geography*. Medical geography is almost becoming a subject in its own right.

(d) *History*. The history of marriage, drugs, etc. to help to get things in perspective. The health habits of whatever period is being studied.

(e) *Mathematics*. An understanding of simple statistics that can be applied to health. Meaningful figures could be used for graphs and percentages and the pupils could be helped to understand their meaning. Household budgeting, mortgages, insurances, hire purchase. The cost of having a child.

(f) *Languages*. The health and habits of the people whose language is being learned and a comparison with ours.

(g) *Religious and/or Moral Education*. The ethics of marriage, parenthood, illegitimacy, abortion, contraception, petting, drug-taking, the power-urge etc.

(h) *Drama*. This could take the place of the mediaeval Courts of Love as a training or practice for life. Role playing can teach through feeling and can extend a child's emotional as well as mental horizons.

(i) *English*. Literature is of vital importance in health and social education. It is easy to give the facts about reproduction but more difficult to convey the emotions involved in 'falling in love'. By reading about someone else's experience, however, it is possible to get a glimpse into what it means. Identification with fictional characters eases the loneliness which many young people feel. Meeting characters with similar defects or failings also consoles and helps the young person to come to terms with his/her own personality.

The idea here is not thematic teaching with every discipline doing 'drugs' at the same time; such a method would drive the pupils mad (or to drink?). Each subject teacher would have to be continually aware of his responsibility for health education and be on the lookout for ways in which it could be fitted naturally into his subject matter. Unfortunately such an awareness is far from universal and even those teachers who may be aware of the possibilities open to them are usually far too busy with examination syllabuses to explore those possibilities. Whilst in many ways this diffusion of health education would be ideal, it is also, in our present atmosphere, impossible. Perhaps in fifty years' time, when health education has an old and established place on the time-table and everyone is aware of its importance, then we can start working towards its integration into the various disciplines. Meanwhile those teachers who are aware of its importance can make a valuable contribution in the context of their own subject.

2. Co-ordination of Subject Specialists

This would need at least one full-time trained health educator to act as coordinator. This scheme makes use of the existing skill and talents of the school staff. Various selected staff members, perhaps from the biology, physical education, English and home economics departments, would be withdrawn from their departments for part of the week and seconded to health education. Whilst this method is working successfully in many schools it is very dependent on the knowledge and interest of the seconded staff. If they lack enthusiasm for their new role then they can so easily nullify the whole venture.

3. A Department of Health Education

My first reaction to this suggestion was negative. It seemed like just another bit of empire building. Further reflection has, however, convinced me that it is the only practical and efficient way of doing it. Health education in the hands of an untrained or unenthusiastic person can be very dangerous. It is a subject which is of vital and particular concern to us all and which can arouse strong emotions in both teachers and pupils. Because of this it needs teachers who are aware of, and can make allowances for, their own prejudices. This is just as important as having the necessary knowledge, and such self-knowledge is difficult to acquire; it needs training.

It will, however, be some time before all schools can have a department of health education with specially trained full-time staff. Our teachers' training colleges are only just starting such training. The best immediate solution lies with full- or part-time in-service courses for teachers who are keen to undertake health education. In some schools the guidance, community studies, or some other department may decide to include health education in their subject. This could be an admirable arrangement providing they realize the full implications of the subject, and the time that will be needed for it. They will also need specially trained staff.

Whatever means a school uses to integrate health education into its curriculum, a great deal of thought must be given to teaching methods. In this subject above all we must avoid didacticism and moralizing. There may be a place for some formal teaching in those areas where the giving of knowledge is a vital precursor to discussion, but it can never be more than a precursor. We want our pupils to change their habits, but we must realize that they will never do so just because we tell them to. Nor can we frighten them into change. Fear is a boomerang weapon. It can produce excellent short-term results but its long-term effect is negligible. Advocates of fear as a teaching weapon often refer to the horror film on venereal disease that was shown to troops during the war. They never seem to ask themselves why, in spite of this film, the incidence of venereal disease was so high among war-time troops. The human mind has the ability to suppress that which it finds too uncomfortable. If we make venereal disease, or anything else, seem too horrific, then people will refuse to envisage the possibility of this terrifying thing happening to them.

This will stop them either from taking preventive action or from seeking treatment. In this way we defeat our own ends.

The only way a permanent habit change can be brought about is to get the person or group concerned to want such a change. The decision must come from them, from their thinking-out of the situation. It cannot be imposed by us. Whilst the ultimate decision must always be an individual one, we must never forget the power of the peer group. None of us is ever completely free from group pressures and they are at their strongest during adolescence. This is something we must never forget. Health is social and emotional as well as physical. If smoking, whether it is cannabis or tobacco, is an essential condition of membership for a particular group then we have got to help our pupils to decide whether the physical risks involved in smoking are greater than the social and emotional risks of being isolated or having to find another group. The answer is seldom clear-cut. Often our only hope is to get a group decision. This, inevitably, makes group discussion one of the most powerful ways of influencing our pupils.

Films, slides, tapes, charts, and books are useful teaching aids. They can help us to convey knowledge in a memorable and easily assimilated way and they can provide excellent discussion-group starters. We need, however, to be very careful how we use them. Different groups of pupils will interpret the same film in very different ways; we should always make sure that they have understood the factual content and discuss their reaction to whatever teaching aid we use. This is true of every subject but it is particularly true here because of the personal and emotive nature of many of the subjects. Nothing clouds and distorts judgement so much as emotions. Health education is dynamite. Let us treat it with respect.

Further Reading

Read, D. A. and Greene, W. H. *Creative Teaching in Health.* (Basingstoke: Macmillan, 1971.)

Project Kit
Health Education – North West Region Curriculum Development Project.

26
Parents, Teachers, and Society

Health education as a school subject needs specially trained teachers but we are all health educators in principle whether we like it or not. Man is a social animal and every time we meet and respond to another person, that person affects our personality. The younger and more malleable we are, the greater the effect on us of the people we meet.

This puts a tremendous responsibility on parents and teachers; it applies to every facet of life, but here we are only concerned with health. Our own basic habits will be frequently copied by the children in our care and bad habits are just as quickly learned as good ones, so that it is easy for us to become ill-health educators. Then there are our prejudices and misconceptions; they are easily caught too. Being an adult among children is a terrifying thing. But perhaps the most important thing of all is the response we expect from them. We are all greatly influenced by expectation. If we expect our young people to respond positively and if our feelings towards them are warm and positive then we have at least a chance of helping and not hindering them.

Every action by a child's parents from the moment of birth contributes to the child's adjustment and education. A clean hygienic house will usually produce clean hygienic offspring, although we must, of course, make allowances for rebelliousness. Warm and loving parents usually produce warm and loving children. Children who feel accepted and valued as themselves will usually accept and value other people for what they are. The way in which a child's first innocent questions about sex are answered will help to form that child's feelings about sex. So will the parental response, or lack of response, to the young child's handling of its genitals. Many parents need help with this early conditioning of the child and this is one of the most valuable roles of the health visitor; she is trained to guide the parent at this time. Often her individual teaching can be re-inforced by group teaching at clinics or health centres. The parents of very young children are usually extremely conscious of their responsibilities and are looking for guidance. Society as a whole has an important role of which many of its members are becoming more conscious. Where community health educators run courses or classes in the various aspects of health, they usually get a good, sometimes an overwhelming, response.

Our job is health education in schools, but the schools are not ivory towers, isolated from the community. Pupils spend only a small part of their time in school. It is easy for our efforts in the classroom to be nullified or even contradicted by the home or the community outside. We can at least lessen the risk of this if we keep the home and community informed about what we are doing. Attention to the mores of the society and to the efforts of other people working in the area are also vital. Co-operation with health visitors, youth leaders, social workers, and anyone else involved in health/social education is essential and they are normally only too pleased to work with us.

Contact and co-operation with and from parents is, however, the most important and most difficult part of our public relations work. The parents need to be kept informed of what we are doing, and if we are to succeed we need their support. The most obvious way of doing this is through a parent/teacher association, the object of which is to provide a channel for this sort of contact. Certainly we should make full use of this method but it is not enough alone. Only a minority of interested and co-operative parents attend regularly. It is, of course, possible to boost the attendance at these meetings by staging special evenings on emotive subjects such as 'sex' or 'drugs', but this is a dangerous procedure that could well do more harm than good. The Grampian Television programme *Living and Growing,* which covers the life cycle of man from birth to old age and which includes a film of an actual birth, is aimed at pupils ten to twelve years old. It is a schools programme but on the evening before the scheduled school showing there is a late night general showing for parents on the normal Grampian network. This is not to allow the parents to decide on the suitability of the programme, with the opportunity of keeping their offspring at home if they disapprove. It is to show them what their children will be seeing the next day, so that they will be able to discuss it with the child. This has been most successful and parents do seem to use it as it was intended to be used. If our schools ran an evening course on the same lines as the ones provided for the pupils, we might find a surprising number of parents attending. They want to help their children and they do not always know how best to do so.

Other channels of communication that we frequently neglect are the mass media – television, radio, and newspapers. They want things that will interest their audience and local reporters will often be glad to do features on work that is going on in schools. They will, of course, only give us space if we can fill that space interestingly. They do not want their readers, listeners, or viewers, and we do not want our pupils, to say 'Oh no, ruddy health again'.

Further Reading

Comfort, Alex. *The Anxiety Makers.* (London: Panther, 1967.)
Linner, Birgitta. *Sex and Society in Sweden.* (London: Cape, 1968.)

Appendix
Suggested Outline Syllabus

First-year Secondary in England – Primary 7 in Scotland

Term 1

1. Simple anatomy and physiology including respiratory, digestive, circulatory, nervous, and reproductive systems and the senses.
2. Relating of above systems to the maintainance of health, e.g. the effect of smoking on the respiratory system.

Term 2

3. To convey a knowledge of the terms used, both professionally and colloquially, for the reproductive organs.
4. Puberty – the physical changes including mentruation, wet dreams, and masturbation. Hygiene of menstruation and 'periods without pain'.
5. How the ovum is fertilized – using charts or models – and how the egg develops into a baby.
6. Birth – using charts or models and a film.
7. Care of the newborn child.

Term 3

8. *Personal hygiene*

    (a) The skin – changes that take place at puberty – and care needed.
    (b) Feet – general care of the feet and the need for properly fitting shoes and socks.
    (c) Hair – general care – head lice and dandruff.
    (d) Teeth – cleaning – diet – dentist.
    (e) Eyes and ears – cleanliness and general care.

Second Year in England – First-year Secondary in Scotland

Term 1

1. Simple first aid for cuts, bruises, burns, and fractures. How to deal with fits and faints. Mouth-to-mouth resuscitation.

Term 2

2. Safety in the home, at school, and on the roads. Expert help may be obtained from the local health visitor and the police.

Term 3

The powerful effect on the body of modern drugs such as penicillin and insulin. The dangers of self-medication with things like aspirins and cough mixtures.

The effect of tobacco and alcohol. A study of the local prevalence of smoking and drinking. Why do people start? Why do they continue?

The need to appear adult – the emotional changes of adolescence.

Third Year in England – Second Year in Scotland

Term 1

Common illness – transmission, prevention and treatment. Hygiene, nutrition, housing, immunization.

The role of public plumbing – including visits to sewage and water works. How to make the best use of our health and social services.

Term 2

Man in his environment. Finite resources, over-population, and pollution.

A study of the destruction of the environment from litter in the playground to napalm in Vietnam, with particular reference to any local problems.

A survey of the area surrounding the school would be interesting.

Term 3

Fitting into the group and living with the family. Why family tensions occur.

The security, and the pressures, of the group.

Group habits.

The effects, physical and psychological, of any drugs being used in the area.

Fourth Year in England – Third Year in Scotland

Term 1

Nutrition and Related Topics

What is food? The constituents of food – proteins, carbohydrates, vitamins, minerals, fats.

Which foods give us what?

What part does each play in the body?

The effects of food on:

(a) A person's appearance; skin (digress to foot hygiene), hair, teeth, and eyes.
(b) A person's growth – height, weight.
    What is growth? Formation of cells, blood, bones.
    The problems and facts of 'adolescent pubertal' growth.
    Eating during pregnancy.
(c) A person's performance – problems and advantages of certain types of food towards performance, e.g. glucose towards sporting performance, alcohol towards physical performance, etc.

What is a balanced diet? Why is it necessary? A study of obesity. Commercial aspects of food.

Term 2

Society and Religion and Contraception. Population and resources. Abortion – natural and induced. This must necessarily be a very shallow treatment stressing that abortion is not a method of contraception. Point out the dangers of abortion particularly back street abortion and any attempts the girl may make to induce an abortion herself.

Sexually transmitted disease: types – stressing the existence of vaginal infections other than venereal disease, signs and symptoms, mode of transmission, precautions, treatment.

158   *Health and Social Education*

Term 3

Addiction

What is a drug? How does it work? How does the body cope with drugs?
How the body's 'defences' can be 'short-circuited'.
 Common drugs, e.g. coffee, tea, coca cola, etc.
 Smoking – present medical evidence – statistics. Social, biological, psychological, commercial aspects. The role of the government. Reasons for and against smoking – a recap.
 Alcohol – Present medical evidence – statistics. Social, biological, psychological, commercial aspects. The role of the government. Reasons for and against alcohol – a recap.
 The drugs of self medication – what are the dangers from what we already know about drugs?
 Drug use – the 'patent medicines' – what are they? What are their effects?
 The 'soft drugs' – what are they? What are their effects?
 The 'hard drugs' – what are they? What are their effects?
 Drugs and society. Drugs and the law.

Fifth Year in England – Fourth Year in Scotland

Drug education

1. Smoking – the psychological and commercial aspects. Why do people smoke? Social habits changing. Pressure of society.
2. Alcohol – physiological effects compared to cultural effects. Drinking as a social habit. Legal aspects including lowering of the legal age, breathalysers. Alcohol addiction – personality defects, escapism, effects on family structure. Why is alcoholism so prevalent in Scotland?
3. Self medication. Dangers of common medicines. The physical effects of common drugs. Principles of correct drug use. Abuse of common drugs.
4. Illegal drugs. Application of same principles as above. Legalization of cannabis – pros and cons. Physiological and psychological and social effects of addiction.

Community health

1. Congenital and genetic defects. Explanations of commonly seen abnormalities, i.e. mongolism, epilepsy, 'spastics', thalidomide, spina bifida, etc. Minor abnormalities, e.g. hare-lip, club foot, hole-in-the-heart, etc. Attitudes of society towards these people, and euthanasia.

2. Minor ailments – the common cold, mumps, measles, etc. Protection against and elementary treatment of.
3. Industrial hazards – safety rules and precautions. Dermatitis, silicosis, pollution of the atmosphere, mercury, lead, etc., poisoning.
4. Some major diseases – cancer, tuberculosis etc., social attitudes.
5. Services available. A study of the Health and Social Services and the benefits available to those in need.

Sex education

1. Sexual relationships and attitudes. Formation of relationships, types of relationships, responsibility of both partners in a relationship.
2. Contraception, pregnancy, and abortion. Where to get advice. Ethics of contraception and abortion, religious views, etc.
3. Unmarried mothers and unwanted pregnancies. Social stigma involved in one-parent family. Pressures on parent and effects on child. Married couples with unwanted children – the planned family. Over-population.
4. Sexually transmitted diseases. Symptoms. Where to get advice. Discussion of 'old wives' tales' etc. Promiscuity – definition and difference between this and a stable sexual relationship. Dangers of promiscuity.

Child care, etc.

1. Birth – the physiological details. Smoking in pregnancy. Psychological effects on mother.
2. Pre- and post-natal care. Diet and exercise, medical care etc.
3. Role of mother and father. Dependence of baby on mother. Consequences of neglect. Father's role in the family.
4. Family structure – relationships between brothers and sisters, effects of a new baby.

Sixth Year in England – Fifth Year in Scotland

This should be an open-ended syllabus, in which discussion can take place freely. The programme is intended to be self-developing, as a result of discussion and interchanging ideas.

Sex education

Developing family – tribalism, polygamy, extended and nuclear families. Refer to Desmond Morris, Willmot and Young.

Relationships and sex. Attitudes – personal, religious, moral. Sex before marriage or not. Sex in marriage. Homosexuality, A.I.D.

Frigidity.

Male and female roles. Traditional and contemporary ideas.

National birth control programmes. Is it clear that countries like China and India need them. Does Britain?

Abortion. Current research. Natural and induced abortion. Attitudes – churches, countries.

Pre-natal aspects of birth, congenital abnormalities. Care of mother's and baby's health. Preparation for birth.

Birth.

Post-natal care of children, physical and psychological dependence.

Drugs

Alcohol, smoking, self-medication, prescribed and drugs of 'abuse'. Current evidence on effects, side effects, short- and long-term effects. International situation, where drugs are made and who sells them.

Drug culture. Does it exist? What is it aimed at? What does it draw on?

The conscious base for a culture.

Statistics of urban and social patterns of drug problems of various kinds.

Youth consciousness

Determining factors. Alienation of youth. Youth and the market. Methods of escape. Social and biological factors in adolescence. Is there such a thing as freedom of choice? Or do we just think we are choosing?

World systems

Ecology, conservation.

List of Useful Addresses

Health Education Index (B. Edsall and Co. Ltd., 36 Eccleston Square, London, SWIV 1PF. Tel 01 828 3016) lists over 3000 aids to health education with a brief synopsis of each together with details of cost and source of supply. It also gives other information such as lists of people who can be called on for help.

Health Education Council, 78 New Oxford St., London, WC1A 1AH, Tel. 01 637 1881. A source of help, information, and material for all health educators in England and Wales.

Scottish Health Education Unit, 21 Landsdowne Cres., Edinburgh, EH12 5EH. Tel. 031 337 3251. A source of help, information, and material for all health educators in Scotland.

Scottish Health Education Council, 21 Landsdowne Cres., Edinburgh, EH12 5EH. Tel. 031 337 7290. Runs staff training courses for all engaged in health education in Scotland.

A.S.H. Action on Smoking and Health, 11 St. Andrew's Place, Regents Park, London, NW1 4LB. Tel. 01 935 7695.

Brook Advisory Centres, 233 Tottenham Court Road, London, W.1. Tel. 01 580 2991.

Family Planning Association, 27 Mortimer Street, London, W1A 4QW. Tel. 01 636 9135.

Marriage Guidance Council, 58 Queen Anne Street, London, W.1. Tel. 01 637 2886.

National Council on Alcoholism, Hope House, 45 Great Peter Street, London, S.W.1. Tel. 01 222 1056.

Office of Health Economics, 162 Regent Street, London, W.1. Tel. 01 734 0757.

Royal Society for the Prevention of Accidents, 52 Grosvenor Gardens, London, S.W.1. Tel. 01 730 2246.

St. John's Ambulance Association, 1/2 Grosvenor Crescent, London, S.W.1. Tel. 01 235 5231.

Index

N.S.U.—non specific urethritis, 109

OBESITY, and the Saccharine Disease,
    10, 11
  causes of, 10, 11
Obsolescence, built in, 144–5
Orgasm, women's, 64

PARENT/TEACHER ASSOCIATIONS, 154
Parental contact, 154
  responsibility, 153
Parenthood, preparation for, 99–105
Parkinson's law, operation of, 5
Peer group, power of, 152
Peptic ulcers, cause and prevention of,
    11–12
  in German army, 12
Periods, painful, 51
Petting, 83
Phenylketonuria, 94
Physical education, 149
'Pill', the, 85–6
Poisons, 120, 122
Police, 46–9, 115, 126
Pollution, 144–6
  modern pollutants, 3, 149
Population increase, 80, 147
Preventive medicine, neglect of, 5–7
Probation officers, 47
Puberty, physical development, 50–53
Public Health Inspector, 115

RELIGIOUS EDUCATION, 150
Ringworm, 117

SACCHARINE DISEASE, THE, 10–13
Safety, home accidents, 127–42
  industrial accidents, 143
  road accidents, 126–7
Scabies, 117
Schofield, Michael, *The Sexual
    Behaviour of Young People*, 69–72
School uniform, 55
Sewage and sanitation, 1, 2

Sex before marriage, 69–75
  education in school, reasons for,
    66–72
  links with primary schools, 72
  in young animals, 69
Sex roles, double standard of behaviour,
    63–4
Sexual abilities, women's, 63–4
  politics, Kate Millett, 61, 64
  potential, female, 64
    male, 64
Sexuality, adolescent, 70–75
  auto, 57, 73
  hetero, 73
  homo, 73
Sexually transmitted disease, 106–11
Shoes, well-fitting, 125
Sleep, 14–15
Smoking, the Government's role, 26
  no-smoking zones, 25
  reasons for, 29–30
  rights of individual and society, 25–6
  risks from, 27–9
Social workers, 114–15, 47
Social work departments, 114–15
Society's role, 153, 154
Sterilization, male and female, 83–6
Syphilis, 107–8

TAMPONS, use of, 52
Teaching aids, use of, 152
Teeth, 123

VD., 106–11
Varicose veins and the Saccharine
    Disease, 10
Vasectomy, 83, 85, 86
Verruca, 117
Vision, defects of, 119
Vitamins and minerals, importance of,
    13

WATER, piped, 1, 2
Watt, Ian, sex in the eighteenth century
    novel, 68
Wet dreams, 51, 52